Contents

KU-545-454

Tables

Figures

Acknowledgements

The monitoring team at the National Foundation for Educational Research would like to thank on behalf of themselves and the APU the large number of people who played a part in enabling the survey reported here to take place and who contributed to the work involved in producing this report.

At the NFER Mrs B Bloomfield and her colleagues Mrs A Baker and Mrs M Hall in the Monitoring Services Unit were responsible for all matters pertaining to contact with the LEAs and the schools which took part in the survey. The statistical analysis of the results was guided by members of the Technical Committee and, in particular, by Mr B Sexton and his colleague Mr P Smedley.

A number of colleagues at the NFER, members of the Monitoring Group, made helpful comments on the initial draft of the report as did Dr I Wells of the Northern Ireland Council for Educational Research. Members of APU Committees, the Steering Group on Mathematics, the Advisory Group on Statistics and the Consultative Committee, have read and discussed the initial draft and their recommendations have greatly contributed to the final draft of the report.

Successive versions of the text and various amendments have been typed with much patience and skill by our secretary Mrs A Watson and typists Mrs J Fisher and Miss K Maychell.

We are again indebted to the schools which participated. Many of the heads and teachers in these schools made helpful comments on the content and presentation of the test materials. We should also like to thank the Local Education Authorities who nominated teachers to be testers in the practical mathematics survey. These teachers (listed in Appendix 4) wrote extremely valuable critiques of the tests which will make a substantial contribution to the development of this innovative form of assessment.

Summary of report

1 This report is the second in a series which will aim to present a national picture of the mathematical performance of 11 year olds in England, Wales and Northern Ireland. It covers the survey carried out in 1979, and includes some comparisons with the results of the 1978 survey. Individual pupils, schools or local education authorities are not identified, and it will be for others to comment on the levels of performance revealed by the assessments.

Second primary survey (Chapter 1)

2 In the 1978 survey, written tests were administered to a representative national sample of about 13,000 11 year old pupils in England and Wales. In 1979, because the sample was extended to include Northern Ireland, about 14,500 pupils were involved. The written tests were the same as those used in 1978 except that a few items were amended to take account of comments made by teachers whose pupils had taken part in the first survey. A sub-sample of about 1,000 pupils also took a practical test and a further sub-sample of about 1,500 pupils completed an attitude questionnaire.

The practical tests (Chapter 2)

3 Whereas in the 1978 survey the emphasis was placed on the measurement of pupils' skills and knowledge, in 1979 more stress was placed on the exploration of pupils' reasoning and understanding of mathematical ideas. Ten topics were assessed, four of them identical to those used in 1978 and the remainder being either new topics or topics amended from the previous year. One important change in the 1979 survey occurred in the emphasis placed on a child's behaviour after his initial response to a question. Testers were encouraged to question pupils who pursued unfruitful paths of action and to probe their misconceptions. This resulted in more pupils achieving success after tester intervention than in 1978.

4 The outcomes of the practical tests are reported in Chapter 2 by means of tables and verbal reports which, by their nature, are not susceptible of further summary. Eight topics are reported, ranging from the strictly utilitarian (for example weighing) to the abstract mathematical (geometric shapes), demonstrating the wide variety of activities undertaken by pupils in the primary school classroom. There is some

comparison of the results over the two years, and results are also reported for practical topics which were not covered in *Primary survey report No. 1,* and have not been repeated in the second survey.

Attitudes to mathematics (Chapter 3)

5   A further sub-sample of about 1,500 pupils were required to respond to a set of 42 statements about mathematics in general (in terms of liking, difficulty and usefulness) and to a set of 34 mathematics topics which they rated in terms of liking and difficulty. They were also asked to state whether or not they had encountered each topic listed. Finally, pupils were given the opportunity to offer their opinion of the questionnaire. Approximately 10 per cent took this opportunity to comment, and were clearly pleased that their views were regarded as important.

6   Pupils' answers were categorised on scales of liking, difficulty and utility, and the results obtained are compared with those of the 1978 survey. Boys' and girls' scores are also compared. Although girls' and boys' total scores are similar, some interesting dissimilarities are revealed, especially in the responses to those statements concerned with the difficulty of mathematics. Results here suggest that at age 11, boys already indicate greater self-confidence in mathematics than girls. In contrast, there are very few differences between boys and girls in their reactions to statements concerning their enjoyment of mathematics, and both sexes seem to recognise the utility of mathematics. In general, the topics 'time' and 'measuring' were the most liked, and were also regarded as being the easiest.

The written tests: sub-category scores and background variables (Chapter 4)

7   Although the written tests which were administered to pupils participating in the 1979 primary survey were the same as those used in 1978, there were some significant changes in the marking strategies adopted. In order to take account of these changes, which in some cases affected the average difficulty of a test, or indeed of a sub-category as a whole, test scores were scaled rather than expressed as a percentage of correct responses.

8   This chapter shows the overall mean scores achieved by pupils in each of the 13 sub-categories of mathematics covered by the tests. A series of tables and figures also gives details of those scores analysed by six sets of background variables (size of 10-plus age group, pupil/teacher ratio, percentage of pupils taking free school meals, school location, region and sex of pupil), and the results are set alongside those reported for 1978. The

results raise interesting questions which deserve serious consideration and further analysis, but the material needs to be treated with great caution. It is important that the discrepancies in mean score between the groupings of the background variables should be interpreted in the light of the much larger differences occurring between pupils within the groupings. Furthermore, the variables are not all independent, and although comment is made concerning some of the major interactions between them, the relationships between the background variables and performance must be interpreted with care. Finally, as with all studies based on the use of correlation, a causal relationship cannot be assumed simply because a strong association is reported between any particular background variable and performance.

The written tests: analyses of item clusters (Chapter 5)

9   Analysis of the data from the 1979 survey revealed that as far as individual items in the sub-categories were concerned, the overall picture of performance was much the same as it was in 1978 and is therefore not repeated in this report. Instead, this section contains some interpretations of pupils' responses to clusters of items of related content. Although pupils' written responses to single items do not offer the immediate access to their thinking in the way that the practical test interviews do, a more detailed picture of the features which affect pupils' performance begins to emerge when the error analyses for a number of printed items of related content are considered along with the proportions of correct responses and rates of omission. The analyses highlight those features of the items which presented pupils with difficulties and also give some indication of the strategies used by pupils to tackle the questions.

The survey results (Chapter 6)

10   As far as the practical tests were concerned, there were few statistically significant differences in responses to items included in both the 1978 and the 1979 surveys. However, this applies only to pupils' initial responses to questions. Tester intervention, which followed the initial response, was rather more searching in 1979, and higher aided success rates were recorded. In the written tests, comparisons made on scaled scores from the two surveys showed that statistically significant changes in mean scores between the two years occurred only in the two computation sub-categories (whole numbers and decimals and fractions). This section, however, stresses the fact that survey data is subject to random fluctuations, and states the importance of distinguishing these from differences which are due to real changes in scores. Although the probability of a statistically significant difference arising by chance is, in

this case, less than 1 in 20, the possibility does exist, and no valid conclusions about trends in performance can or should be drawn from the results of only two annual surveys.

1 Second primary survey

Primary survey 1979

*Mathematical development.
Primary survey report No 1.
HMSO, 1980, price £5.00

1.1 This report is an account of the results of the second survey of the mathematics performance of 11 year old pupils in schools in England and Wales; the results also include, for the first time, those of 11 year old pupils in schools in Northern Ireland. Some comparisons are made with the results of the first survey conducted in 1978*.

1.2 The second survey took place in May 1979 and was conducted by the NFER on behalf of the Assessment of Performance Unit (APU) at the Department of Education and Science. The work is sponsored by the DES, the Welsh Office and the Department of Education for Northern Ireland.

1.3 As in 1978, written tests were administered to a representative national sample of pupils in the age group. Separate sub-samples of the main sample also took either practical tests or attitude questionnaires.

1.4 In 1979 the size of the main sample was about 14,500 pupils and the increase of about 1,500 pupils over the 1978 survey is due to the participation of Northern Ireland pupils on this occasion. About 10,500 pupils were from English schools, 2,000 from Welsh schools and 2,000 from schools in Northern Ireland. Nearly 1,000 schools were involved in the survey.

1.5 The 26 written tests given to the pupils were the same as those employed in 1978 except that a few of the 647 items were amended to take account of comments from teachers of pupils in that survey. These changes were mainly cosmetic and were made, for example, to arithmetic signs in some items which in the 1978 survey were thought to be ambiguous and to items which had indistinct graphic features.

1.6 Each test consisted of a different selection of items from three of the thirteen sub-categories of mathematics in the assessment framework (see Figure 1.1). The framework has been amended in one respect: 'applications' no longer appears among the categories of learning outcomes, and categories of context (mathematical, everyday, and other subject) have been added to those of content and outcome. The applications of number sub-category is now seen as testing concepts and skills in an everyday context. This is a change in classification only and not in the assessment materials.

1.7 The tests were taken anonymously and were administered in the same fashion as in 1978 so that individual pupils, schools and authorities could not be identified.

1.8 In the practical mathematics survey 10 topics were assessed, four of them identical to those used in 1978. The remaining six topics were new or amended from the previous year. The tests were administered by 26 experienced teachers of 11 year olds nominated by their local authorities and trained to administer the tests by the NFER monitoring team. Up to six pupils were tested in each of the 200 schools in the practical survey sub-sample.

Figure 1.1 *Assessment framework*

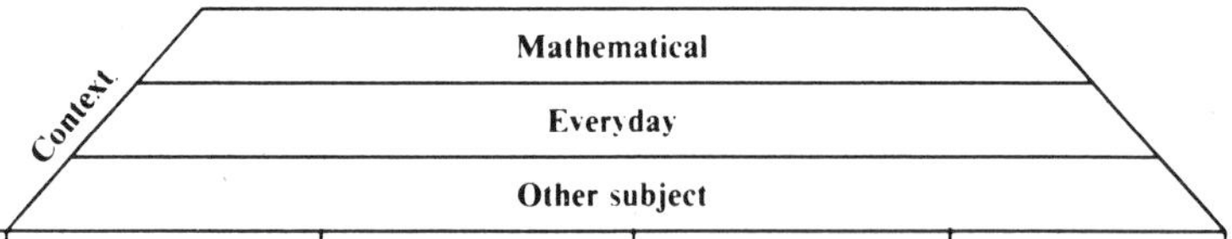

Context	Mathematical			
	Everyday			
	Other subject			

Content \ Outcome	Concepts	Skills	Outcomes of Problem Solving and Investigating	Attitudes
Measures	Money, time, mass, temperature		To be included from 1980 in practical tests and from 1981 in written tests.	Liking, difficulty and utility of mathematics / Liking and difficulty of mathematical topics in the sub-categories
	Length, area, volume, capacity			
Geometry	Shapes, lines, angles			
	Symmetry, transformations, coordinates			
Number	Concepts: natural number	Computation: naturals and decimals		
	Concepts: decimals and fractions	Computation: fractions		
	Applications of number			
	Rate and ratio			
Algebra	Generalised arithmetic			
	Sets and relations			
Probability and Statistics	Probability and data representation			

Each outcome can be assessed in either written or practical (interactive) modes

1.9 The attitude questionnaires used in the 1979 survey were unchanged. Pupils were asked to respond to statements about their liking of mathematics, how difficult they found it and how useful they thought it to be. They were also asked to indicate which mathematical topics they liked or disliked and found easy or hard. Six pupils from each of 200 schools in the sub-sample took attitude questionnaires in 1979. The number of pupils participating in the assessment of attitudes to mathematics was similar to the previous year but was drawn from a larger number of schools so that the sub-sample on this occasion was more broadly representative than in 1978.

New features of the reporting

1.10 *Primary survey report No. 1* presented and commented on the full width of the picture provided by the results, with a consequent lack of some detail. The emphasis in this second report has been to analyse and comment on selected areas of mathematics in greater depth. Some range has been given to the content by sampling topics from each of the five main categories of the assessment framework.

1.11 In Chapter 2, which is concerned with the results of the practical tests, detailed accounts are given of topics from the categories of geometry (shape), 'measures (weighing and angles) and probability and statistics (probability and data representation). Chapter 5 is an account of the responses given to some item clusters in the written tests from the categories of geometry (bilateral symmetry), number (decimals, adding and subtracting fractions), and algebra (generalised arithmetic). Also included in this chapter is a description of pupils' responses to some items from the number, measures and probability and statistics categories which are concerned with reading graphs and scales. The reporting of both written and practical tests is orientated more towards pupils' understanding of mathematical concepts and procedures on this occasion than in the first primary survey report.

1.12 Another aspect of the reporting this time is that some comparisons of the data from the two completed surveys have been made. These can be found in Chapters 2 (practical tests), 3 (attitudes) and 4 (sub-category scores and background variables). A new feature of the reporting of the results within bands of the background variables in Chapter 4 is that the sub-category scores are given in scaled units for both the 1978 and 1979 survey data. The scaling procedure used is fully described in Appendix 3.

1.13 In summary, this second report on the mathematical performance of 11 year olds fills in some further details of the overall picture of performance. Some comparisons have been made between the results of the 1978 and 1979 surveys, but no valid conclusion about trends can be drawn from only two surveys.

2 Practical tests

The practical surveys

2.1 The one-to-one interviews, which come under the general description of practical testing, are unique in national assessment programmes. In the narrowest sense, they can be regarded as assessments of the practical skills that form a part of the primary curriculum. They may also be regarded as measures of the extent to which pupils can apply their mathematical knowledge to practical situations. However, because of their nature, consisting of a dialogue between experienced teacher and pupil, they afford an opportunity for the exploration of children's reasoning and understanding of mathematical ideas. In the initial survey the measurement of skill and knowledge was emphasised. However, in the 1979 survey more stress has been placed on the third aspect of practical testing, namely the exploration of pupils' reasoning and understanding by the tester.

2.2 Formally, the tests followed the pattern established in 1978. Indeed, four tests were identical. As in 1978, all possible efforts were made to ensure that the administration of the tests was standardised throughout the sample. Testers were instructed to ask the questions as phrased in the scripts although they could probe the pupils' understanding of these questions. They were also given detailed instructions on the presentation of the testing materials. Acceptable and unacceptable responses were clearly delineated. In summary, the conditions in which the practical test items were initially put to pupils remained the same in both years and the results may be regarded with confidence for purposes of comparison.

2.3 One change that did occur was in the emphasis placed on pupils' behaviour after their initial response to the question. The instructions given to the testers implied that unfruitful paths of action should be questioned and that misconceptions should be explored. As a result, more pupils achieved success after tester intervention in 1979 than in 1978. A comparison of the scripts from the two years showed a marked discrepancy in the "flavour" of the testing. It was evident that, under questioning from the tester, many pupils rectified their initial errors in judgement or strategy. Sometimes simple questions such as, 'How did you get that?', led pupils to reconsider their initial response and to spot for themselves inconsistencies in their thinking. For this reason, the proportion of pupils giving an acceptable reply after discussion with the tester, previously termed *aided success,* is not strictly comparable between the two samples. Consequently, only initial responses are recorded in the comparisons made in paragraphs 2.14 — 2.86.

2.4 A final caveat concerns the accuracy of the results reported. As a general rule the size of the sample determines the confidence with which the mean score of the sample can be viewed as an estimate of the mean score for the population from which the sample was taken. The larger the sample, the smaller will be the band of scores around the mean score of the sample in which the score for the population as a whole is most likely to lie. This band of scores is called the confidence limits.

*Whenever the words "significant" or "statistically significant" are used in this chapter they refer to statistical significance at the 5 per cent level. Note that this does not necessarily imply educational significance (see Appendix 2).

†This is not the case in the probability topic.

In the case of the written tests a large number of pupils are tested. Fewer pupils take each of the practical topics, and consequently the confidence limits are quite wide. This fact is taken into account when the statistical significance* of differences in performance between years and between sexes is determined. It is also reflected in the test where the percentages are rounded off to the nearest 5 per cent†. However the tables give the mean percentages obtained by the samples to the nearest 1 per cent and it should be noted that the confidence limits for these data can be as much as ±7 per cent. That is there are 95 chances out of 100 that for any particular question the mean for the population as a whole lies somewhere in a band with an upper limit 7 per cent above the reported mean and a lower limit 7 per cent below it.

1979 Survey topics

2.5 In paragraphs 2.14 — 2.86 the results of eight of the ten topics used in the 1979 survey are reported, the results of the remaining two topics (symmetry and number rods) will be given in a subsequent report.

1978 Survey topics

2.6 Although over half of the 1978 topics were repeated in the 1979 survey, three were not used in 1979 and were not discussed in *Primary survey report No. 1.* These results are now reported in paragraphs 2.87 — 2.109.

Design of the 1979 practical survey

2.7 Table 2.1 lists the ten mathematical topics that formed the basis for assessment in the 1979 survey. In order to provide for comparison, four were identical to those used in 1978 (mass, length, fractions, angles). Three (money, visualisation, geometric shapes) were revised or extended from the previous year, while three (number rods, probability, symmetry) were new.

2.8 Although the tests varied in content, some contained similar concepts and skills. The topics also varied in difficulty and it was not unlikely that the degree of difficulty presented by the initial topic might affect pupils' attitudes and subsequent achievement. In order to take account of any learning or motivational effects, each topic was placed in different positions and in different contexts in each test in which it appeared. Consequently, the ten topics were distributed among twelve tests, with three topics appearing in each test. No test contained the same three topics and each topic appeared in a different position in each test. Table 2.2 gives the complete design.

2.9 Since the testing was arranged so that up to six pupils would be seen in any one school, the tests were divided into two 'day packs', each containing a different set of six tests. The administration of these 'day packs' was balanced among the testers. For example, on any one day during the survey half of the testers were administering Day Pack A whilst the other half were administering Day Pack B. In turn, half were administering the tests in sequential order, while the other half were administering them in reverse order.

The testers

2.10 Local Education Authorities nominated 26 testers to take part in the survey. Twenty-two of these were from England, two were from Northern Ireland and two from Wales. Pupils in Wales had the option of being tested in Welsh by a bilingual tester.

Table 2.1 *Practical topics used in 1979 primary survey*

Main content category	Practical topic	Sub-category of curriculum framework
Number	*Fractions* fractions of continuous and discrete objects (string and plastic shapes)	Number concepts (decimals, fractions)
	Number rods using number rods to find a pattern in the partitions of whole numbers	Number concepts (whole numbers)
Geometry	*Geometric shapes* classifying shapes: practical application of knowledge of shapes	Lines, angles, shapes
	Angles estimating and measuring angles	Lines, angles, shapes
	Visualisation constructing brick models from diagrams	Lines, angles, shapes
	Symmetry recognising and constructing symmetrical patterns	Symmetry, trans- formations, co- ordinates
Measures	*Money* giving change	Money, time, mass, temperature
	Weighing weighing blocks and plasticine using balance	Money, time, mass, temperature
	Length estimating straight and curved lines, measuring	Length, area, volume, capacity
Probability and statistics	*Probability* predicting and recording the outcomes of chance events	Probability and statistics

2.11 The testers were trained at a two-day residential conference held in April 1979. In addition they practised giving the tests to pupils in their own schools. These practice runs were reviewed and commented upon by the monitoring team in order to ensure a high degree of standardisation in the testing procedure.

The pupils

2.12 The tests were administered to pupils in 204 schools during the two weeks from 2 May to 17 May. In all, approximately 1,200 pupils were tested, each taking three topics.

The tester — pupil interaction

2.13 After putting the pupil at ease, the tester was required to read the initial item from the coding sheet. If the pupil did not respond or the answer given was incomplete the tester was asked to encourage the pupil or to clarify the initial question. Similarly, if a method or explanation was required but not evident in what the pupil said or did, the tester was asked to probe for a clear account of the pupil's strategy or reasoning. If an answer was given which was not listed as acceptable on the coding sheet, the tester prompted by encouraging the pupil or providing some helpful information. The interaction was terminated with an acceptable response from the pupil or a decision by the tester that further probing or prompting would prove unfruitful or would harry the pupil. The data from each item were coded in terms of the interaction itself. Pupils' responses and methods were coded before and after tester intervention. The amount and type of intervention by the tester was also coded. Unless noted, the responses that are cited in the report are those recorded before tester intervention.

Table 2.2 *1979 practical survey design*

Test Design
Topic Code Letters

M. Money
W. Weighing
L. Length
S. Symmetry
R. Number rods
P. Probability
G. Geometric shapes
F. Fractions
A. Angles
V. Visualisation

		Position in test									
Test No.	Topics:	M	W	L	S	R	P	G	F	A	V
1	M W L	1	2	3							
2	S R P				1	2	3				
3	G F A							1	2	3	
4	V M R	2				3					1
5	P G W		3				1	2			
6	L S F			1	2				3		
7	F P M	3					2		1		
8	W A S		1		3					2	
9	R L G			2		1		3			
10	A V P						3			1	2
11	M S G	1			2			3			
12	W F V		1						2		3

Results of 1979 survey topics

Probability

2.14 Although the formal theory of probability is not generally considered appropriate for primary school pupils, most curricula do include some graphical recording of chance events. Presumably these concrete activities set the stage for later abstractions. By gathering evidence and recording it appropriately, children learn to organise material. It is this organisation that forms the basis for the abstractions and generalisations of later formal work. Although termed 'probability', this topic was not confined to the assessment of 11 year olds' understanding of that notion. It was also designed to assess their ability to hypothesise, to record and explain data and to use those data as a basis for generalisation to future events. Basically, it was composed of two parallel investigations: one which presented two possible outcomes (the tossing of a coin); the other, six outcomes (the rolling of a die). In each case, pupils were asked to predict results that might be obtained over a specific number of instances. They were next required to test their predictions and record the results. Finally, they were asked to comment on the results obtained and to generalise to future instances. The pattern of responses that occurred was similar in both investigations and can be discussed in terms of ability to predict, record and generalise.

The coin:
two outcomes

Prediction

2.15 When pupils were presented with a coin and asked to predict the number of heads that would turn upmost after 12 tosses, most answered in terms of the number of possible outcomes, ie. over 60 per cent of the 404 pupils who took this topic predicted that heads would come up six times.* Asked to justify their prediction, almost all of these pupils stated explicitly that six was half of 12 or, more generally, cited the number of alternatives. In addition, some pupils went on to qualify their original prediction by stating that six was an average or by referring to the element of chance. 'It could be anything, but about six. There are two sides to the coin so both have an even chance.' However, it was clear that others regarded their predictions with greater certainty. At this stage, these pupils were not willing to acknowledge the possibility that chance might affect results, a typical response being, 'Every time you toss, it should land on a different side because it's got to go alternately.' Conversely, slightly over 10 per cent of the pupils apeared to ignore completely the number of alternatives in determining their predictions. When questioned, these pupils usually referred to past experience ('It always comes up tails'). Disappointments seemed to be more clearly remembered and were more frequently cited. 'When I'm throwing a coin into the air it lands on heads more than tails. I always go for tails and I always seem to lose.'

Recording

2.16 Pupils were next asked to confirm their predictions by tossing the coin 12 times. They were presented with a choice of plain or squared paper on which to record their results. Although less than 10 per cent actually drew a block chart, the majority of the pupils chose the squared paper, using its features to construct some type of graphical presentation. For example, over a third of the pupils listed the outcomes in two separate columns. Occasionally, the actual results were recorded, as in Figure 2.1: more often, tallies were made (Figure 2.2).

---

* Because of the more exploratory nature of the topic, with its emphasis on explanation rather than factual information, a table of exact results is not given.

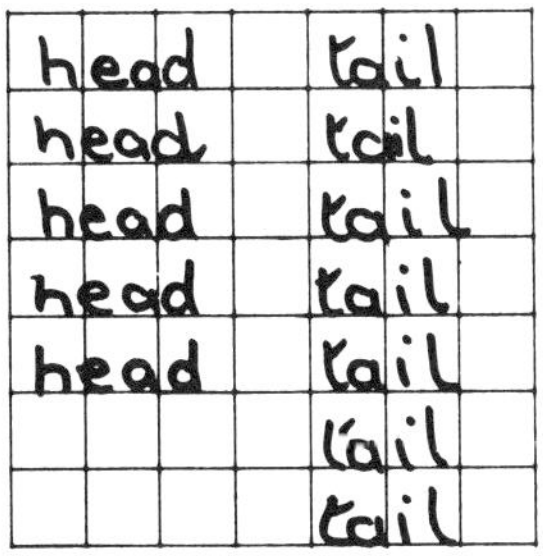

head	tail
head	tail
head	tail
head	tail
head	tail
	tail
	tail

Figure 2.1

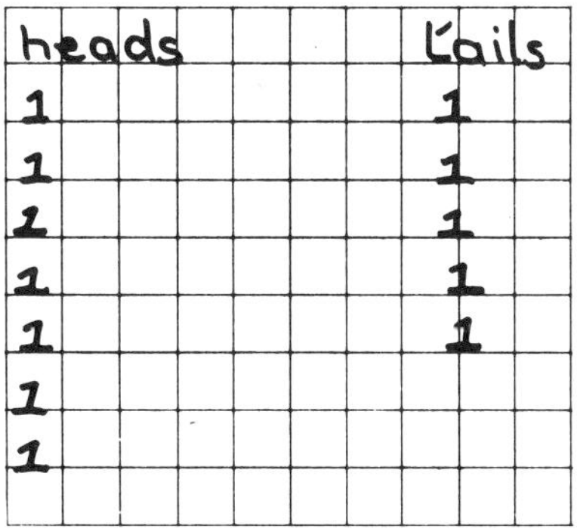

heads	tails
1	1
1	1
1	1
1	1
1	1
1	
1	
1	

Figure 2.2

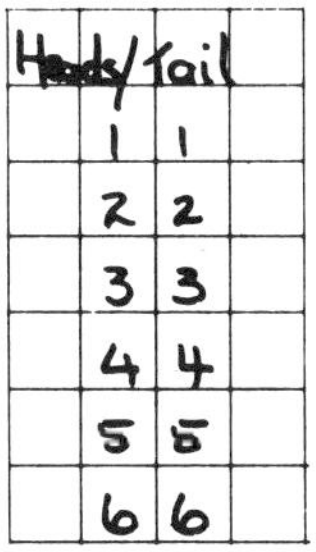

Heads/Tail	
1	1
2	2
3	3
4	4
5	5
6	6

Figure 2.3

2.17 Although the relative frequency of heads or tails is obvious from the length of the respective columns on these charts, the number of times the coin was tossed is not readily apparent.

2.18 In constructing these records, pupils were obliged to keep a mental count of each toss. However, some pupils overcame this difficulty by indicating the frequency of each occurrence under the appropriate column (Figure 2.3).

2.19 In contrast to these graphical presentations of the material, at least one third of the pupils listed the outcomes in a single column as they occurred. Most of the pupils who chose this method attempted no type of labelling. As a consequence, these pupils not only had to keep track of the total number of tosses, but had to keep separate count of the number of times each side of the coin turned up, since none of this information was obvious from their recording. Some overcame this problem by listing the number of the toss next to each result. (See Figure 2.4).

2.20 Although these two broad categories — a single column of outcomes and two separate tallies — accounted for the majority of efforts, there were variations within each. Initial choice of paper appeared to be related to the clarity of presentation. Results recorded in plain paper were generally less obvious than those written on squared paper. On the other hand, squared paper did not ensure clarity. Some pupils neglected to label their results, and others grouped results or recorded horizontally rather than listing them in columns.

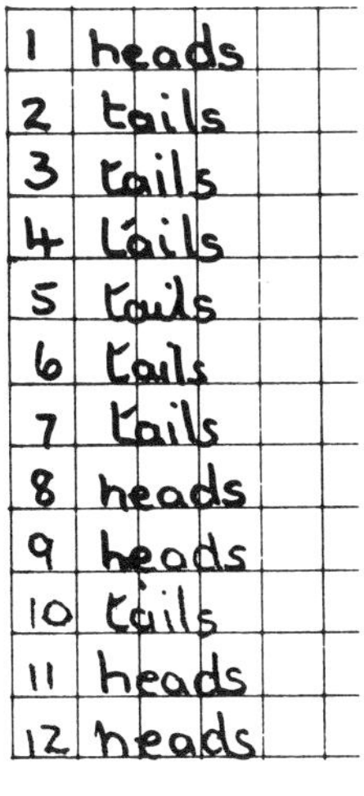

1	heads
2	tails
3	tails
4	tails
5	tails
6	tails
7	tails
8	heads
9	heads
10	tails
11	heads
12	heads

Figure 2.4

Generalisation

2.21 When the coin was tossed 12 times with varying results, pupils were again asked to comment on their predictions in the light of the results obtained. Of those pupils whose predictions were not confirmed, 80 per cent expressed surprise. Conversely, 80 per cent of the pupils whose predictions were confirmed were surprised. Many of these pupils stated that their prediction of six heads was not to be regarded as an exact estimate but as an average. The answers of other pupils seemed to imply that their original prediction (6 heads) had been an 'official response' that they themselves had little confidence in. One pupil, who obtained six heads after predicting six, confessed to the tester, 'I only guessed that it would be six and six. I didn't think it would do it.'

2.22 When probed, pupils experienced difficulty in generalising on the results. Approximately 10 per cent did not respond to the question, 'why are you surprised (not surprised) by the results?' Another 15 per cent justified their reaction by referring to the specific results obtained (eg 'There were only 2 heads, I thought there would be more.') Others stated that they had guessed. However, over half the pupils were able to make some general statement on the basis of the results obtained. Their responses appear to fall into three broad categories.

1. Responses which referred to the random element in the tossing of the coin. These responses were usually from pupils who had predicted a specific number of heads but had not expected that exact number of occurrences. Approximately 15 per cent of the responses fell into this category. Typical of these responses were such statements as: 'Six was an average sum and the results weren't too far out.' 'I suppose it's just the luck of the draw. I was thinking of the mathematical chances.'

2. Responses which appeared to ignore the element of chance, stressing the belief that the alternatives should appear with equal frequency. Approximately 25 per cent of the responses fell into this category. Typical among them were: 'I thought it would come down an even number.' 'It usually comes down equal times. It spins in the air and when it comes down it's the opposite side.'

3. Responses which appeared to ignore the mathematical basis for prediction, attributing results to an outside force — either chance or personal magnetism. Approximately 15 per cent of the responses fell into this category. Many of these pupils had predicted a specific number of heads or tails other than six. For them heads or tails appeared to hold a special force. 'My brother usually gets more tails' or 'My coins always land on heads' was the usual justification for their original predictions and most of these pupils expressed surprise when these were not confirmed. Sometimes however, as in the following case, lack of confirmation did not weaken the original belief. Predicting three heads and getting six, one pupil expressed surprise, explaining, 'It's unusual for it to be the same. Tails always come up more often.' Asked if he would expect the same results with a fresh round of 12 tosses, he replied steadfastly, 'No, I don't think it can happen twice. Next time tails will win.' Others were less sure. Asked why he wasn't surprised that his prediction was not confirmed, one pupil answered with resignation, 'I didn't think there was much chance of me getting it right. If I had got it right I would have been surprised.'

2.23 When asked whether the results would be the same in a repeated run, 75 per cent said 'No', 15 per cent 'Yes'. The rest were unsure. Again, pupils experienced difficulty in justifying their reasoning. 20 per cent maintained that the results were different each time. Ten per cent said that it depended on how the coin was tossed, and the same percentage made some reference to luck. No clear pattern emerged from the remainder of the responses. Answers ranged from 'My dad can make a coin come up when he wants to' to 'It's all in the luck of the toss.'

The die: six outcomes

Prediction

2.24 Much the same pattern of response occurred when pupils were asked to predict and generalise about the die, although fewer pupils gave the theoretically correct answer when asked how many times each number might be expected to turn upmost in 24 throws.

2.25 In the case of the coin, it was possible to justify the mathematically correct answer by reference to physical actions. Pupils referred to the fact that the coin turns in the air, and many appeared to believe that heads and tails would alternate. Indeed, with an invariant odd number of turns in the air, heads and tails must appear an equal number of times. However, no such physical model exists for a 6-sided die. Although pupils might be aware that the 'mathematically correct' answer to the question is four, their 'common sense' led them to believe that such an occurrence was unlikely. For this reason, perhaps, 15 per cent fewer pupils were willing to predict an equal number of appearances for each number on the die. On the other hand, a sizeable proportion predicted specific numbers based on their previous experience with games involving dice. Others believed that the person throwing could control the number that appeared upmost on the die. More than one pupil spoke of rolling it fast or slow.

Recording

2.26 There was more need for organisation in the recording of the rolls of the die than in the toss of the coin and, in turn, the task produced more variable results.

2.27 Over a third of the pupils labelled columns 1 to 6 and recorded results under the appropriate column. The choice of squared paper seemed to encourage pupils to represent the distribution in a visually coherent manner. Although relatively few pupils (less than 5 per cent) recorded their results in the form of a block graph, as in Figure 2.5, the layout of the paper itself obviously influenced presentation. Figure 2.6 represents a popular method, with the pupil using the squares on the paper as a form of place holder. Others used only the horizontal lines on the paper, tallying results in a less regular fashion. (Figure 2.7)

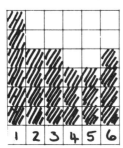

Figure 2.5

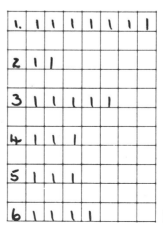

Figure 2.6

2.28 Generally, those who chose the plain paper (approximately 30 per cent of the pupils) tended to have less orderly presentations of the results. However, as illustrated in Figure 2.8, some pupils presented the information clearly and concisely.

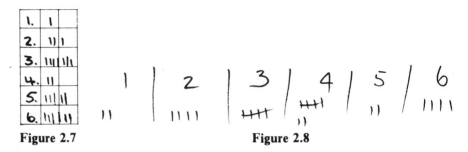

Figure 2.7   **Figure 2.8**

2.29 The majority of pupils, realising the need for organisation, numbered the columns before they began the task of rolling the die. Others were less organised. In their enthusiasm to begin rolling the die, they labelled each column at the time when the number first appeared. In some cases, such as the one described below, possible problems were recognised.

"She began throws with a 1 and a 2. The child made a mark on the top corner for 1. At the second throw she made another mark next to it. At this point she realised that she couldn't tell whether it was for a 1 or 2 or any other number and realised also that the problem would be even greater if other numbers appeared.

She began to put numbers above the marks and I suggested that she 'spread out' a little."

2.30 Of course, only the relative frequency is apparent from the above methods. The absolute frequency of any number has to be worked out from the chart. Even those pupils who constructed block graphs rarely labelled the vertical axis. The one method which overcame this difficulty was followed by 15 per cent of the pupils. It is illustrated in Figure 2.9. Here the number of times that a number occurred at any point in the series of rolls is readily apparent.

1	2	3	4	5	6
1	1	1	1	1	1
2	2	2	2	2	2
3	3		3	3	3
4	4		4		4
5					5
6					

Figure 2.9

2.31 All of the above methods focussed on the results achieved by rolling the die. None recorded the number of times the die was rolled. Pupils who appeared to respond to this latter aspect of the task were among those 30 per cent who made a single list of outcomes, writing down the numbers as they occurred. At least 10 per cent of this group labelled each throw. If they could not easily see the frequency of each number, at least they were continually aware of how many times they had rolled the die. A few, possibly not realising the advantage of graphical representation, carefully recorded each result verbally. Figure 2.10 represents such a recording.

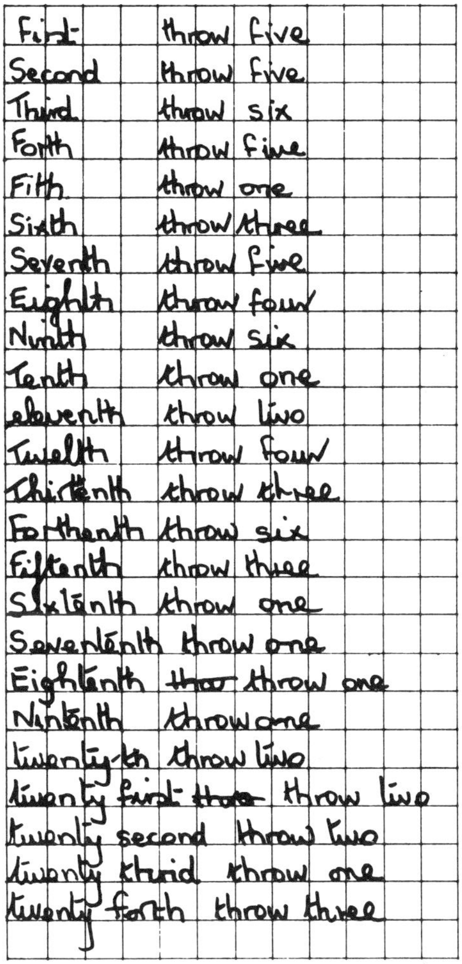

Figure 2.10

2.32 Although the above summary represents the vast majority of responses, there were unique efforts that did not fall into the general pattern. Many of these attempts were unsuccessful. On the other hand, some were original presentations in which the necessary data was clearly and economically presented. Figure 2.11 represents one such effort.

Generalisation

2.33 The pattern of responses to the die investigation fell into the same general categories as those observed in response to the coin. However, perhaps because of the number of possible outcomes, many pupils tended to discuss the results in terms of specific numbers. The discussion of these results seemed to reveal most clearly the pupils' ability to generalise. When asked whether a fresh run of the die would bring the same results, the large majority of the pupils said 'No'. (85 per

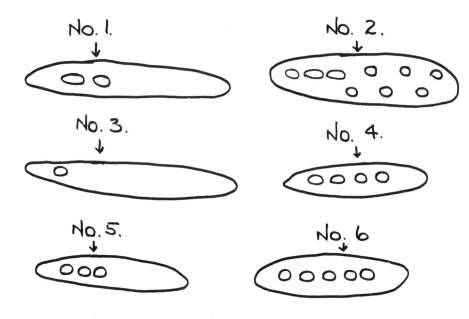

Figure 2.11

cent as opposed to 75 per cent in the case of the coin). Forty per cent stated flatly that the results would be different each time, while 10 per cent maintained that the results depended on how the die was thrown. Conversely, another 10 per cent stated that it was all a matter of luck. The following exchanges illustrate the wide range of responses among the pupils tested.

Pupil A   This pupil had predicted that each number would come up 'roughly about four times'. Asked if he was surprised at the results that he obtained, he replied, 'A bit. . . . but they're roughly the same. So not really.'
'Would you expect the same results again?' asked the tester.
'It's like a 1 in 50 chance.'
'What does that mean?' asked the tester.
'That's just a term I use. If you did something 50 times, then you would only expect it to happen once.'

Pupil B   This pupil, having predicted that each number would appear four times, expressed surprise when his results showed wide variability. 'I rolled it fast or sometimes slow', he explained.
'Did that make a difference?' asked the tester.
'A bit. Every time I rolled it fast, it went on a 4, except once it went on a 3.'
'Why do you think that happened?'
'I don't know. I wish I did.'
The tester pursued the subject. 'Do you think you would get the same results if you rolled again?'
'I might. It might go the same again. Might not. It all depends how I roll it.'

2.34 Finally, the pupils were asked which was the easier to predict, the face of a coin or the number on a die. Approximately 10 per cent chose the die, mainly on the grounds that the die had 'more numbers to choose from'. The others chose the coin, with most citing the smaller number of alternatives as the reason for their choice. The high percentage of pupils who were able to apply this fundamental notion of probability to an actual situation is in sharp contrast to results on a similar question on the written test to which 50 per cent of the pupils responded correctly. Although this may reflect the difference between the practical and the written testing situations, the experience gained in the course of the topic may have contributed to pupils' success.

Summary: probability topic

2.35 In general, the results show a disparity between the quality of predictions and the justification given for them. The vast majority of pupils gave mathematically sound predictions which were based on the number of alternatives and the number of occurrences. However, when they found that these predictions were not confirmed by the data, many pupils reverted to past experience, hunches or cynicism for justification of the results. The more mathematically minded, perhaps more articulate, child was able to accommodate the discrepancy between theory and practice. Although seldom using technical terms such as 'random' and 'odds', these pupils either qualified their original predictions by referring to 'an average' or, in later discussion, showed that they appreciated the role of chance. Other pupils became confused, either clinging to what they believed must be the mathematically correct answer despite contrary results, or abandoning theory altogether. To many pupils the test was a new experience, one in which there was no right or wrong answer. Whether because it did not conform to their idea of a 'test' or because they lacked the necessary vocabulary to express their ideas, some pupils found the need to justify their beliefs a disconcerting experience. As one tester remarked, 'Why do you think that? seems an unusual question for most of them and some were quite nonplussed.' She adds, 'Speaking as a teacher . . . . it's a question we should put a lot more often!' Beyond this, the test itself gave insight into pupils' ability to organise data and to use it in support of their predictions.

Geometric shapes

2.36 In this topic pupils were encouraged to discuss the properties of quadrilaterals and to apply their knowledge of shape practically by making a label for a food tin. In the first instance, pupils were presented with 9 quadrilaterals including a square, a parallelogram and a trapezium. (see Table 2.3). Their task was to pick out the rectangular shapes from the set and to explain the reasons for their choice.

2.37 Almost all of the pupils tested (90 per cent) readily picked (a) and (b) as rectangles. However, the recognition level dropped somewhat when the shorter sides of the rectangle lay along the horizontal axis. This less familiar position appeared to confuse some pupils. Almost 15 per cent rejected (i) as a rectangle, while approximately 20 per cent rejected (d). One pupil justified his exclusion by stating that these shapes were 'oblongs'. Others insisted that rectangles 'lie down' and that rectangles are 'flat, long and not very wide'. The confusion of position with geometric attributes is reflected in this interchange between a tester and pupil.

2.38 After the pupil had rejected (d) as a rectangle, the tester rotated the card through 90°.
'Is it a rectangle now?' he asked.
'Yes, it is,' the pupil replied.
'Just because I turned it round?'
'Yes,' insisted the pupil.
The tester next rotated the figure back to its original position.
'Is it not a rectangle now?'
'No' replied the pupil. Then, reconsidering, he changed his mind. 'Yes, it is.'

2.39 More generally, the relative salience of position in 11 year olds' recognition of shapes is confirmed in the written tests. For example, when presented with two rectangles, one of which had been rotated through 45°, 15 per cent of the pupils failed to recognise that the rectangle which lay in the oblique position was identical to the standard (horizontally positioned). A similar percentage failed to recognise an irregular quadrilateral when it was rotated obliquely. That the percentage remained comparable in the case of this less familiar shape suggests that position itself exerts a strong influence on recognition.

2.40 The relative dimensions of the figure also presented difficulties to some pupils. For example, almost 15 per cent rejected (f) as a rectangle. Common among the reasons given for rejection was that it was 'too thin'. One pupil gave as a general rule, 'A rectangle is about twice the size of a square'. Another suggested that rectangles were 'like squares but a steam roller has flattened them'. On the other hand, despite this reference to squares, squares were not generally regarded as rectangles. Most pupils made a clear distinction between the two. One tester commented, 'No child included a square in the selection of rectangles and a few were even outraged that one should contemplate such an act'. This observation is borne out by the total results. Over 80 per cent of the pupils excluded (g) from their set of rectangles, while approximately 35 per cent excluded (c). In some cases (c) may have been excluded because, at first glance, it may be mistaken for a square. On further questioning, almost 10 per cent of those pupils who had initially rejected (c) changed their minds, mainly on the grounds that they had taken it to be a square.

2.41 The rejection of the square and square-like shape reflects pupils' conviction that a rectangle is a shape in which 'two sides are longer than the other two' — a remark that was recorded for approximately 15 per cent of the pupils. Indeed, when pupils were asked to give their criteria for classification of a shape as a rectangle, most tended to focus on the relationship between opposing sides of the figure rather than on adjoining sides. For example, over 50 per cent of the pupils referred to the fact that the opposite sides of rectangles were equal in length. Approximately the same number mentioned parallel sides. In contrast, only 20 per cent initially made explicit reference to 90° angles, with a further 10 per cent stating that rectangles must have 'straight sides'. As one tester noted, 'Most (pupils appear to recognise intuitively that right angles are involved but apart from a minority, after prompting, they could not verbalise their thoughts and ideas on this point.' After prompts, a further 10 per cent of the pupils added right angles to their criteria; however, the fact that the parallelogram was accepted as a rectangle by 25 per cent of the pupils, with some shifting of opinion in both directions even after prompting, does indicate that pupils do not consider the angles of the figure a primary feature in determining a rectangle. That the opposite sides of the parallelogram are equal in length and parallel were considered to be sufficient conditions for its inclusion in the set of rectangles. The parallelogram also presented a possible source of confusion between the three-dimensional shape which the child internalises and the two-dimensional one that is presented on paper. For example, one pupil explained his inclusion of the parallelogram in his group of rectangles by referring to the image produced by drawing a rectangle in perspective. 'I know that rectangles have straight lines, but if you look at it like a top of a table, this (the parallelogram) could be one.'

2.42 On the task as a whole, boys were more accurate than girls in their classification of shapes as rectangles. As a total score, the difference was slight, but differences did occur in the case of individual shapes. More girls than boys failed to recognise (b), (c) and (i) as rectangles. In contrast, there was no difference in the percentages who rejected the parallelogram and the trapezium. See Table 2.3 for complete results.

2.43 Pupils were next asked to relate their knowledge of two-dimensional shapes to a three-dimensional one. Presented with a cuboid, they were asked to indicate which of their original set of shapes corresponded to the faces of the cuboid.

2.44 Slightly more than half the pupils correctly identified all three rectangles. Although some pupils made the wrong choice, most errors appeared to result from a lack of recognition of the three-dimensional aspect of a solid shape. For example, a quarter of the pupils chose only one rectangle — in most cases (a), which corresponded to the face with the largest area and was, therefore, the most obvious of the three faces. Although 10 per cent of the pupils were eventually taught the correct shapes, most rectified their initial mistake after prompting and were able to identify all correctly, saying that two of each would be needed to cover the cuboid.

2.45 As a final task, the pupils were presented with two tins (one empty, the other to be used as a model, full of baked beans), paper, pencil, ruler, scissors, string and tape measure. Their task was to make a label for the empty tin.

2.46 The pupils seemed to enjoy this part of the test and proceeded to work with reasonable competence and efficiency, as the tester noted their strategy. There were few pupils who needed help in recognising the basic requirements of the task. Only 5 per cent did not realise that a rectangular shape was needed. Most pupils quickly set about measuring the required height and circumference. The tape measure was used most frequently, although many pupils switched to a ruler in order to determine the height of the tin. However, a great variety of methods were recorded. For measuring the circumference pupils used string and ruler or string only; they rolled the tin along the paper or used a combination of tape measure and ruler. For measuring the height of the tin the majority of the pupils used either the ruler or the tape measure, but some used the string, the tin itself, or both tape and ruler.

Table 2.3 *Pupils' classification of shapes**

Shape			Percentage choosing shape as rectangle	Percentage choosing shape as non-rectangle
a		All	91	6
		Boys	93	4
		Girls	89	8
b		All	91	6
		Boys	94	3
		Girls	87	10
c		All	60	36
		Boys	64	32
		Girls	56	41
d		All	78	18
		Boys	81	16
		Girls	75	21
e		All	15	82
		Boys	15	81
		Girls	15	82
f		All	84	13
		Boys	85	12
		Girls	82	14
g		All	8	88
		Boys	8	88
		Girls	9	88
h		All	25	71
		Boys	26	71
		Girls	25	72
i		All	82	14
		Boys	86	11
		Girls	78	18

* 402 pupils took this topic.

2.47 Testers noted that at least 10 per cent of the pupils checked their efforts at some point during the test and they judged that the resulting labels fitted around the tin with reasonable accuracy in 42 per cent of the cases. Very few of the pupils were unable to carry out the task. In almost 20 per cent of the cases, both length and width were judged to be inaccurate. Either one or the other was inaccurate in the remainder of the cases. The judgement of testers and the pupils themselves concurred to a remarkable extent as can be seen from the following table. After the task had been completed, the tester judged the results and, without referring to his judgement, asked the pupil if the label fitted the tin. If it did not, the tester asked why.

TESTER		PUPIL	
(Judgement of accuracy)		(Response to: "Does it fit?")	
Unable to complete	5	Not applicable	5
both l and w accurate	42	Yes	47
Width inaccurate	19	No: width inaccurate	13
Length inaccurate	12	No: length inaccurate	12
both l and w inaccurate	18	No: l and w inaccurate	10
		No: other features	8

When pupils recognised an inaccuracy, most were able to say what they had done wrong (usually a matter of inaccurate measurement rather than of strategy).

Angles

2.48 This topic, like many others, was concerned with both understanding and skill. It investigated pupils' ability to recognise the properties of angles, particularly right angles, and to use a protractor in the measurement of a series of angles.

2.49 As a first step, testers established pupils' familiarity with basic terminology. Using a hinged angle maker, (Figure 2.12) testers displayed an angle, enlarged it and asked 'What are angles measured in?' Over half the pupils gave the correct term immediately, while less than a quarter were unable to reply. The remainder gave a variety of answers, with approximately 10 per cent suggesting 'centimetres'. Although some pupils recalled the correct term after prompting, 40 per cent were eventually taught.

Figure 2.12   **Figure 2.13**

2.50 The testers next used the angle maker to demonstrate a right angle, (Figure 2.13), which was recognised immediately by 55 per cent of the pupils. Twenty per cent did not respond or stated that they did not know the name, while the remaining 25 per cent gave a variety of incorrect answers. As in the case of the previous question, 40 per cent were taught that the angle made by the tester was called a right angle.

2.51 The success rate rose with the next question. When asked how many degrees there were in a right angle, approximately 60 per cent of the pupils answered correctly. Evidently some pupils who had forgotten the name of the angle remembered its properties when the name was supplied. This level of success is comparable to that achieved on a similar item in the written tests, where pupils were presented with a drawing of a right angle (without identification as such) and asked to estimate its size. 60 per cent of the pupils gave the correct answer of 90°.

2.52 When the tester rotated the arm of the angle maker to inscribe a circle, most pupils (80 per cent), perhaps learning from the previous questions, correctly stated that it was turning through four right angles. Fewer (60 per cent) were able to translate this information into the correct number of degrees.

2.53 The focus of activity shifted from the tester as pupils were given an irregular sheet of paper which they were to fold twice in order to make a right angle. This proved to be an easy task for most pupils, with over 80 per cent making the second fold at a right angle to the first. However, having folded the paper correctly, fewer pupils were able to show the resulting right angle and to mark it correctly.

2.54 The pupils were next asked to divide their folded angle in half and to state the number of degrees in the resulting angle. This task was accomplished successfully by the majority of pupils. However, approximately one third did not respond to the request that they divide the *angle*. Instead of dividing the angle (a), they attempted to halve the area of the paper by folding along its perimeter (b). The difficulty of these pupils in forming a 45° angle is not suprising when one considers that almost a quarter of the pupils had been unable to identify the initial right angle.

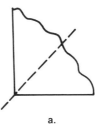
a.

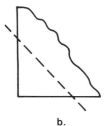
b.

2.55 The next series of questions were intended to investigate pupils' ability to use a protractor for the measurement of angles. Because of the variation in school equipment, three types of protactors were provided; semi-circular, circular and a tru-fit angle indicator.

2.56 Most pupils acknowledged some familiarity with one or more of these instruments and just over 40 per cent called them by the correct name. 'Compasses', 'projectors' and 'rectiles' were some of the names suggested. On the other hand, once the correct name had been established the majority of the pupils replied immediately that they were used to measure angles or degrees.

2.57 The pupils were asked to choose one of the three protractors in order to measure a series of angles. Undoubtedly reflecting its use in schools, the semicircular protractor was chosen by the great majority of the pupils (80 per cent), although some pupils were more adventurous, choosing a protractor which they said they had not used before.

2.58 Each pupil was presented with one obtuse and three acute angles. The first angle (Figure 2.14) was measured accurately by 40 per cent of the pupils. Of the remaining pupils, 20 per cent attempted to measure the angle but incorrectly positioned both zero and the intersection of the protractor. A further 20 per cent stated that they did not know how to go about the task. Testers had been advised to teach the use of the protractor on the first occasion if necessary, and approximately 40 per cent of the pupils were taught.

2.59 When presented with the second angle (Figure 2.15), 47 per cent of the pupils measured it successfully. That facility on these two tasks is comparable, despite the fact that different scales must be used for each, implies either familiarity with the use of a protractor and/or good judgement of the approximate size of an angle. Less than 5 per cent of the pupils made the obvious error of using the wrong scale and reading the angle as the supplement of its correct value (ie 127° ± 1°).

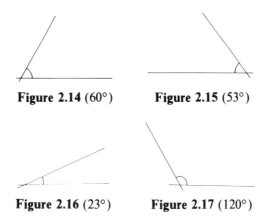

Figure 2.14 (60°)   **Figure 2.15** (53°)

Figure 2.16 (23°)   **Figure 2.17** (120°)

2.60 Perhaps due to increasing familiarity with the requirements of the task, the success rate rose when pupils were presented with the third angle in the series (Figure 2.16). Approximately 55 per cent of the pupils were correct in the measurement.

2.61 The same proportion of pupils measured the fourth angle accurately, (Figure 2.17). However, another 20 per cent of the pupils read from the wrong scale, giving the answer of 60° ± 1°. This suggests that a distinction can be made between those pupils who are solely proficient at using the protractor and those who, in addition, have some understanding of the relative size of angles. That the latter is not an easy concept for 11 year olds is evident from the results of the written test. Their success at estimating the size of a series of angles was far lower

Table 2.4 *Topic on angles: comparison of successful responses in 1978 and 1979*

		England & Wales	England & Wales	England, Wales & N. Ireland
	Year	1978	1979	1979
	No. of pupils	354	273	303
		%	%	%
1. 'What are angles measured in?'	All	49	54	54
	Boys	47	58	56
	Girls	49	50	52
2. Make 90° angle. 'This particular angle has a special name. Do you know what it is?'	All	58	57	56
	Boys	55	60	59
	Girls	60	54	53
3. 'How many degrees are there in a right angle?'	All	56	62	62
	Boys	51	66	66
	Girls	58	58	58
4. Start with 0°. Turn angle maker round through 360°. 'How many right angles have I turned through by going right round once?'	All	80	80	79
	Boys	78	82	81
	Girls	81	78	78
5. 'How many degrees is that?'	All	53	60	59
	Boys	50	64	63
	Girls	54	56	55
6. Give pupil irregular shaped paper. 'Fold this paper twice to make a right angle.' 'Show me the right angle.'	All	64	71	69
	Boys	63	70	67
	Girls	65	72	70
7. 'Mark it.'	All	58	66	64
	Boys	55	69	68
	Girls	60	63	61
8. 'Now make another fold to divide your right angle in half.' 'How many degrees is that?'	All	40	56	57
	Boys	36	57	56
	Girls	42	56	58
9. Present protractors 'What are these called?'	All	48	43	43
	Boys	48	47	46
	Girls	49	39	40
10. 'Use one of the protractors to measure the angle between these lines.' (60°, Accept ± 1°)	All	42	44	42
	Boys	42	46	44
	Girls	43	42	40
11. 'Now measure this angle.' (53°)	All	35	49	46
	Boys	33	52	50
	Girls	36	46	43

12. 'Now measure this angle.' (23°)	All	37	61	59
	Boys	39	67	65
	Girls	36	56	54
13. 'Now measure this angle.' (120°)	All	37	58	58
	Boys	39	65	65
	Girls	36	52	51

The boxes indicate that the proportions within are significantly different statistically.

than in the practical tasks described above. When pupils were presented with a 120° angle in the written test, only 15 per cent were able to judge its correct size, while 60 per cent were able to give the number of degrees in a right angle.

2.62 Testers also commented on the disparity between pupils' proficiency in the measurement of angles and their understanding of angles' attributes. 'The pupil is very proficient at measuring angles but her responses to probes seem to indicate that she doesn't know what she is measuring, ie, doesn't really know what an angle is.'

2.63 The fact that approximately 20 per cent to 30 per cent of the pupils experienced great difficulty with the questions and had to be taught indicates a basic lack of understanding of the nature of angles. With the exception of the use of the protractor, success on the topic was dependent upon that understanding.

Comparisons with 1978 results

2.64 Among the 1978 topics that were repeated in 1979, the initial responses to the topic on angles showed the greatest change. As discussed in paragraph 2.3, over the practical tests as a whole, the interaction between tester and pupil appeared to increase success substantially in 1979. For this reason aided responses (ie those given after prompting by the tester) were not compared between the years. On the other hand, responses to the initial questions were not affected by the attitude of the testers for there was no overall increase or decrease in the initial success rates between years. The exception to this general rule was the topic on angles. To a greater extent than was true of the other topics, angles consisted of related questions that relied upon the same procedure for success. This applied particularly to the series of questions calling for the measurement of angles, but was also true of those which involved folding the irregular shaped paper. Consequently, comparison of responses between 1978 and 1979 should be looked upon with some caution.

2.65 Table 2.4 illustrates this point. When first asked to measure an angle (Question 10) approximately 40 per cent of the pupils in both years were successful. This suggests that the response to this first measuring task is analogous to the initial responses to questions in the other topics. However, on subsequent tasks, the two years differ. In 1978 the next angle (Question 11) presented more difficulty and fewer pupils were able to make an accurate measurement. The success rate rose marginally on the next two questions. However, at no point did it rise above the initial level of success, implying that these pupils did not learn to use the protractor during testing. At least 35 per cent continued to demonstrate their skill at using the protractor to measure a variety of angles.

2.66 This pattern of responses is in sharp contrast to that found in 1979. Here, after presentation of the first angle, success rose with each successive angle. By the end of the series, approximately 15 per cent more pupils were able to use the protractor than had previously been able to do so. Although testers had been instructed to teach the use of the protractor if necessary on the first occasion, they were told not to teach on subsequent occasions. Although the rise in success in Question 11 may be attributed to explicit teaching, this would not account for the continued rise in success in Question 12.

2.67 This pattern is repeated to a lesser degree in the series of tasks which involve folding the irregular shaped paper. Again, the last question of the series produced a significant difference between the years, with more pupils achieving success in 1979.

Weighing

2.68 This topic explored children's understanding of weighing through the use of a balance scale. Pupils were asked to determine the heaviest of 3 objects of unknown weight, to make balls of plasticine weighing 20g and 10g, and to use the information gained through their work with the balance to deduce the weight of a single plastic shape.

2.69 The first task required the pupils to identify the heaviest of three wooden blocks which were otherwise identical. This proved to be a simple task for most pupils, with approximately 80 per cent of the pupils correctly identifying the heaviest block. However, although the majority of the pupils first balanced two blocks, then balanced the heavier of the two with the remaining block, a sizeable proportion (over 20 per cent) used less efficient methods.

2.70 Some pupils initially experienced difficulty in accepting the notion of balance as a method of determining relative mass. In these cases some prompting by testers usually led to success. The following are typical of such exchanges:

Places each in one tray, one at a time — nothing in the other.
Pupil: 'Do we have some weights?'
Tester: 'No, just the scales.'
The pupil then balances X against Y.
Pupil: 'X is heavier than Y.'
Tester: 'So which is heaviest?'
Pupil: 'Z is heaviest.'

Others needed more explicit prompting to use the scales correctly.

Pupil puts Z in one pan, nothing in other.
Removes Z, replaces with X.
Removes X, replaces with Y.
Pupil (indicating X): 'I think this.'
Tester: 'Why?'
Pupil: 'Because it stays down.'
Tester: 'What do the others do?'
Pupil: 'Stay down, but not as much.'

Tester (pointing to other pan) 'Could you use this side at all?'
Pupil now 'weighs' each in other pan as above.
Tester: 'What would happen if you put one in each pan?'
Pupil now weighs Z and X in turn against Y.
Pupil: 'Z is heaviest because it goes down more than this one (X).'

2.71 When presented with a 20g mass and asked to identify it, 60 per cent of the pupils called it 'a weight' or, more specifically, 'a 20g weight'. Another 25 per cent, possibly misunderstanding the question, replied that it was 20 grams. No pupil called it 'a 20g mass' and only 2 pupils of the 400 tested referred to it as 'a mass'.

2.72 Pupils were next asked to make a lump of plasticine as heavy as the 20g mass. Approximately 85 per cent of the pupils were immediately successful. Although 5 per cent attempted to judge the relative weights by holding the objects, most used the scales, carefully re-shaping the plasticine after each addition or subtraction. Testers noted that small bits of plasticine were added and well worked in before each attempt at balancing the plasticine against the metal mass. One tester remarked, 'I do not remember any child working on this topic who realised that initially they could drop small pieces in and join them at the end'. The summary data support this observation. Only 2 per cent of the pupils were observed to balance separate bits of plasticine against the 20g. Although pupils may have been influenced by the request that they make a 'lump' of plasticine, there is the suggestion that, for the some pupils, density and mass are related in such a way that an increase in the density of an object results in an increase in its mass. For example, testers commented that some pupils appeared to squeeze the plasticine in order to alter its weight. The following exchange is recorded by one tester. The plasticine was heavier than the 20g mass and the pupil was attempting to adjust it.

Tried squeezing all the plasticine and balanced it against the 20g mass (3 times).
Tester: 'What are you doing?'
Pupil: 'Squeezing it.'
Tester: 'Why?'
Pupil: 'To make it heavier.'
Tester: 'Why do you want it to be heavier?'
Pupil: No response.
Tester: 'What will you have to do?'
Pupil (apparently realising her mistake) 'Take some off.'
Eventually balanced but once again tried squeezing to make it lighter.

2.73 Having succeeded in making a ball of plasticine that balanced the 20g metal mass, pupils were asked to make a ball that was half as heavy. This request caused some confusion. Initially, only 30 per cent of the pupils used the balance to divide the plasticine into two accurate parts, each weighing 10g. Possibly influenced by the use of the metal mass in the previous question, 45 per cent of the pupils did not recognise that the plasticine itself could now be used as an adequate 20g measure. Another 20 per cent divided the plasticine in half visually, with no reference to the balance. In these cases, a question such as, 'How do you know that the two pieces are exactly the same?' was usually followed by the use of the balance as a check for accuracy. After clarification or prompting by testers, a further 45 per cent of the pupils divided the plasticine accurately. However, 10 per cent did not succeed after prompting and a further 10 per cent were taught the correct procedure. Many of the pupils who did not succeed remained convinced that the 20g standard weight was vital to the solution of the problem. The difficulty experienced by these pupils is exemplified in this exchange. The pupil divides the plasticine visually, then asks for the weight. He puts the 20g weight in one tray, the plasticine in the other tray until it begins to lift the other end of the scale.

Tester: 'If that's half, what's that?' (Points to the remainder of the plasticine.)
Pupil: 'It should be half.'
Tester: 'And do you think it is?'
Pupil: 'No.' (Tries again, still unsuccessful.)
Tester (pointing to the 20g): 'Did this help you?'
Pupil: 'Yes.'
Tester: 'Could you have managed without it?'
Pupil: 'No.'

2.74 Finally, testers noted an occasional confusion among pupils about their notion of balance or, more specifically, how to correct an imbalance. When asked to use the balance to divide the 20g of plasticine into two equal parts, some pupils were observed to take pieces from the lighter side and/or add them to the heavier. In contrast, once pupils had discovered the correct strategy, they had little trouble in giving the weight for each half. About 85 per cent stated correctly and without prompting that each half weighed 10g.

2.75 Finally, the pupils were presented with the 20g mass and a bag of identical plastic shapes and were asked to find the weight of one (5g) shape. This more complicated problem was solved correctly by approximately half of the pupils. Testers' observations of the difficulties experienced by those pupils who needed help is of interest. For example, some pupils responded initially to the question by balancing a single shape against the 20g mass. As one tester suggested, 'They did not see the relationship of the weight to more than one shape. The fact that the scales did not move for one shape was an important part of this misunderstanding'. Perhaps more significant, however, was the tendency of pupils 'to get stuck on the physical side'. They appeared to experience difficulty in shifting from one level of operation to another; that is, to use the information gained through physical manipulation as a basis for mental calculation. This tendency to rely on practical experience alone is illustrated in the following interchange between a pupil and tester.

20g weight in one pan. One shape added to other pan.
Pupil: 'It weighs about 5g.'
Tester: 'How do you know?'
Pupil: 'It doesn't weigh as much as the 20g. It feels lighter than the 10g.'
Tester: 'It might be 3g or 6g.'
Pupil: 'If it were 3g it would be as light as a feather.'
Tester: 'Think of a way of finding out what it weighs exactly.'
Pupil: 'Can you use all the shapes?'
Tester: Yes. (More shapes added to the pan)
Pupil: '4 weigh 20g.'
Tester: 'I want to know the weight of one.'

Pupil does not reply.
Tester: 'If 4 weigh 20g, one weighs?'
Pupil: '5g.'

2.76 On the whole, pupils performed very well on this topic, after initial difficulties were overcome by hints or prompts from the testers. Testers also liked the topic — believing that it combined the use of practical equipment and problem solving at an appropriate level.

2.77 Table 2.5 compares the differences in successful responses between the two years. In 1979 pupils appeared to experience particular difficulty in answering Question 3. Despite the fact that testers had been instructed to hold the 20g mass in their hands while explaining the task, many pupils attempted to use the metal mass. Since the strategies used by pupils were not recorded in 1978, it is impossible to compare the relative frequencies of different methods between the years.

Table 2.5 *Topic on weighing: comparison of successful responses in 1978 and 1979*

			England & Wales	England & Wales	England, Wales & N. Ireland
		Year	1978	1979	1979
		No. of pupils	365	366	400
			%	%	%
1.	Present scales and three wooden blocks. 'Use the scales to find out which of these blocks is heaviest.'	All	74	79	79
		Boys	84	82	83
		Girls	69	76	75
2.	Present 20 g mass. 'Make a lump of plasticine that is as heavy as this 20 g mass/weight.'	All	80	84	83
		Boys	84	86	86
		Girls	78	82	79
3.	Hold 20 g mass in hand. 'Make a lump of plasticine that is *half* as heavy as this 20 g mass/weight.,	All	40	29	29
		Boys	46	29	30
		Girls	37	29	28
4.	'What does each half of the plasticine weigh?'	All	84	83	84
		Boys	83	82	83
		Girls	85	83	85
5.	Present 20 g mass again. Present bag of shapes. 'Use this 20 g to find out what *one* of these plastic shapes weighs.'	All	54	49	49
		Boys	58	55	57
		Girls	52	42	40

The boxes indicate that the proportions within are significantly different statistically.

2.78 Differences in performance between boys and girls showed no consistent pattern in the two surveys. In 1978 significantly fewer girls than boys were successful at using the scales to determine the heaviest of three blocks. In 1979, although still relatively less successful than boys in completing the task, the difference between the sexes was not sufficiently large to be considered significant. On the other hand, in 1979 significantly more girls found difficulty in determining the weight of a single plastic shape. Analysis of the methods employed indicated that almost twice as many girls as boys initially attempted to balance a single plastic shape against the 20g mass. This suggests that the difference in success rate on the question can be largely accounted for by inappropriate strategy on the part of girls.

Table 2.6 *Topic on fractions: comparison of successful responses in 1978 and 1979*

			England & Wales	England & Wales	England, Wales & N. Ireland
		Year	1978	1979	1979
		No. of pupils	381	358	392
			%	%	%
1.	'Cut this string in half.'	All	86	86	90
		Boys	83	80	85
		Girls	92	92	94
2.	Pick up one piece. 'Now cut off ¼ of this piece'.	All	64	72	71
		Boys	60	66	67
		Girls	71	78	76
3.	'What fraction of the whole string that you started with is that little string?'	All	42	41	43
		Boys	43	40	41
		Girls	40	43	40
4.	Present 3 yellow and 3 red squares. 'What fraction of these squares is red?'	All	61	56	57
		Boys	58	59	59
		Girls	66	52	54
5.	Present 3 yellow and 1 red square. 'What fraction of these squares is red?'	All	64	67	67
		Boys	65	65	66
		Girls	61	68	68
6.	Present stapled bag. 'Estimate what fraction of these pegs is white.' (14 white, 45 coloured pegs.)	All	61	61	61
		Boys	61	60	61
		Girls	60	62	62

The boxes indicate that the proportions within are significantly different statistically

Fractions

2.79 The Fractions topic tested pupils' ability to recognise fractions as part of a continuous length and of a discontinuous quantity. Specifically, pupils were asked to cut a piece of string in half, then to cut off a quarter of the remaining half. Next, they were asked to name the fraction represented by a subset of a collection of tiles. Finally, they were assessed on their ability to estimate in terms of fractions.

*Mathematical development.
Primary Survey Report No 1.
HMSO, 1978, price £5.00.*

2.80 A full description of the topic and results obtained in 1978 can be found in the first primary survey report*. Table 2.6 compares the percentage of successful responses for the two years.

2.81 As in 1978, girls performed the two tasks that required cutting the string more accurately than did the boys. Analysis of the methods employed showed that boys were more likely to estimate visually while girls folded the string end-to-end before making the cut. However, there was no difference in their ability to recognise the relationship between their final product and the original length of string. (see Question 3.) In 1979 girls' performance on the next question was significantly lower than in the previous year. Almost 15 per cent of the pupils tested gave '1/3' as the answer. Evidently the combination of equal quantities proved more difficult than when the quantities were unequal (Question 5).

Length

2.82 The topic on length was described in detail in the 1978 report. Briefly, pupils were asked first to estimate, then to measure a series of line segments (see Figure 2.18). Results for the two years are presented in Table 2.7. After the initial question, pupils in the current survey gave consistently more correct responses to the items; however, in no case is the difference large enough to reach a level of statistical significance.

Figure 2.18 *Topic on length: lines to be measured*

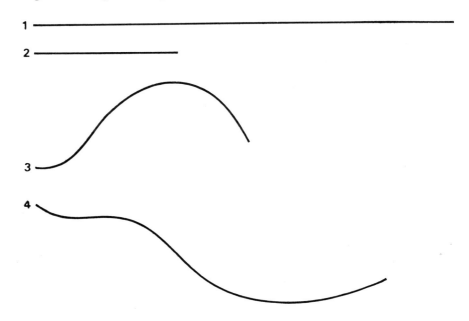

(The lengths of the lines above are not exactly as specified.)

Table 2.7 *Topic on length: comparison of successful responses in 1978 and 1979*

		England & Wales	England & Wales	England, Wales & N. Ireland
Year		1978	1979	1979
No. of pupils		381	279	305
Straight Lines				
		%	%	%
1. 'Estimate the length of line 1.' (accept as successful: 10 to 16 cm)	All	69	63	63
	Boys	70	65	65
	Girls	67	61	59
2. 'Estimate the length of line 2.' (3 to 6 cm)	All	79	82	83
	Boys	79	81	81
	Girls	78	84	85
3. 'What could you use to see if your estimate was right?'	All	96	92	93
	Boys	95	91	92
	Girls	98	94	95
4. 'Measure line 1.' (13 cm)	All	84	86	87
	Boys	83	88	89
	Girls	86	84	84
5. 'Measure line 2.' (4.5 cm)	All	85	89	90
	Boys	85	90	91
	Girls	84	88	90
Curved Lines				
6. 'Estimate the length of line 3.' (6 to 10 cm)	All	83	88	89
	Boys	83	86	87
	Girls	84	89	90
7. 'Estimate the length of line 4.' (8 to 15 cm)	All	80	84	85
	Boys	78	82	82
	Girls	84	86	87
8. 'Measure line 3.' (8 cm $\pm$ 0.5)	All	75	80	80
	Boys	74	78	79
	Girls	77	81	82
9. 'Measure line 4.' (12 cm $\pm$ 0.5)	All	76	81	81
	Boys	75	80	81
	Girls	78	82	82

Visualisation

2.83 The visualisation topic was essentially the same as that employed in 1978, although the order of presentation differed. As in 1978, a series of diagrams of five models was presented. Pupils were required to construct each in turn, using a set of wooden cubes.

Figure 2.19 *Topic on visualisation: diagrams of models.*

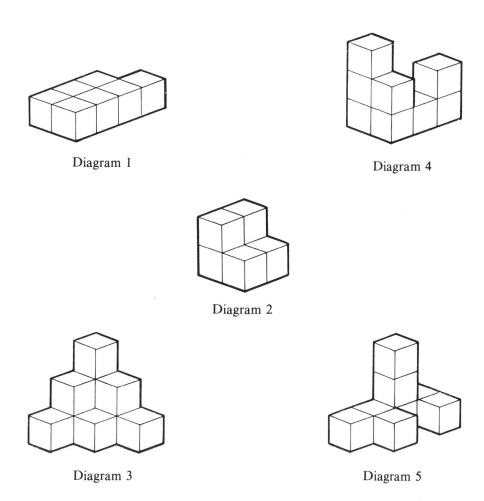

Diagram 1

Diagram 4

Diagram 2

Diagram 3

Diagram 5

2.84 Table 2.8 indicates that pupils generally found little difficulty in interpreting most of the diagrams. However, it appears that the two diagrams that did present some difficulty differentiated between the sexes in both years. Girls found both tasks more difficult than boys. Detailed analysis of the unsuccessful responses to Diagram 3 gives some indication of the source of their difficulty. The diagram itself appeared to puzzle many girls. Almost 10 per cent of the girls (compared with less than 5 per cent of the boys) needed encouragement before attempting the task at all. Of those who did respond, more girls than boys, failing to recognise the depth of the model, omitted one or more of the diagonally placed cubes. Girls were also more likely to align cubes face to face rather than at an angle to one another.

Money

.2.85 The topic on Money was extended in 1979 to include an item requiring that change be given from a £1 note. Pupils' methods of giving change were noted. Table 2.9, which compares results obtained in the two surveys, indicates little difference in the pattern of responses.

2.86 The added item, used in the 1978 survey of 15 year olds, required pupils to deduct 32½ pence from a pound. Although appreciably more difficult than the previous tasks, 50 per cent of the pupils were successful compared with 91 per cent of the 15 year olds. Most pupils correctly counted on from 32½ pence. The half-pence accounted for most of the errors, with pupils tending to forget or ignore it in their calculations. This occurred more often in the case of those pupils who mentally subtracted 32½ pence from a pound in order to determine the correct change.

Table 2.8 *Topic on visualisation: comparision of successful reproduction of diagrams in 1978 and 1979*

		England & Wales	England & Wales	England, Wales & N. Ireland
	Year	1978	1979	1979
	No. of pupils	180	270	297
		%	%	%
Diagram 1	All	96	96	96
	Boys	98	96	96
	Girls	96	95	96
Diagram 2	All	99	96	95
	Boys	100	96	96
	Girls	98	95	95
Diagram 3	All	61	72	72
	Boys	77	81	82
	Girls	54	65	63
Diagram 4	All	88	81	81
	Boys	96	87	86
	Girls	84	76	76
Diagram 5	All	91	99	98
	Boys	88	99	98
	Girls	92	98	98

The boxes indicate that the proportions within are significantly different statistically.

Table 2.9 *Topic on money: comparison of successful responses in 1978 and 1979*

			England & Wales	England & Wales	England, Wales & N. Ireland
		Year	1978	1979	1979
		No. of pupils	175	366	403
			%	%	%
1.	Give pupil 50p coin, teacher keeps the rest. 'That 50p coin is yours, these coins are mine. If you want to pay me 10p show me how to do it.'	All	88	92	92
		Boys	82	91	92
		Girls	91	93	93
2.	'Now you've got four 10p coins and three pennies; 'If you want to pay me 17p, show me how to do it.'	All	93	91	91
		Boys	88	92	92
		Girls	96	90	90
3.	'Now you've got two 10p coins and three pennies; that's 23p. If you want to pay me another 17p show me how do it.'	All	64	63	62
		Boys	60	62	62
		Girls	66	63	62

1978 Survey: Results of topics not released in Primary survey report No. 1.

2.87 These topics were not used in the 1979 survey and were not reported on in *Primary survey report No. 1*. In that report details were given of the aided and unaided success and that procedure has been followed for the topics reported in this section.

Problem-solving strategies

2.88 The problem was typed on a slip of paper and presented to each pupil taking this test. It read as follows:

> A construction company makes steel bars in two lengths 6m and 9m. These bars cannot be cut but they can be joined end to end to make longer bars. What lengths of bar can be made up to 30m long?

2.89 The main focus of the assessment was the extent to which pupils used some systematic method of finding combinations of lengths, and were able to give a valid reason for being able to state whether or not they had found all possible combinations. The testers were asked to judge whether pupils were fully, largely or partially systematic in searching for combinations, but the guidance given to them on placing pupils' responses in these categories proved insufficiently clear for reliable judgements to be made. Consequently no statistical summary is given here and the following account gives details only of the range of responses made by pupils.

2.90 If, after being presented with the problem, the pupil was unable to proceed, the tester asked whether there was anything that was not understood. The meanings of words could be explained (for example, 'construction company') or the rules of the task clarified.

2.91 At this stage only pencil and paper were available, but if the pupil was still unable to make any progress after clarification of the task, the tester produced some 6 unit and 9 unit number rods and demonstrated how a 15 unit length could be made by placing them together end to end. Then the pupil was asked to make up some more lengths and record the lengths made.

2.92 There were variations in the notation used to write down the combinations found. A few pupils drew the rods on the paper provided but many used numerals only to indicate lengths and addition signs for a combination (eg. 6 + 6 + 9). Conjuction of numerals was also used to indicate a combination by one pupil:

66666;
9966.

2.93 Multiplication symbols were written by some pupils when only one length was involved in a combination (eg. 3 x 6) or some verbal equivalent was employed (3 sixes). Several examples were noted where both x and + were used in a mixed length combination (eg 2 x 6 + 9). The following oral account was provided by one pupil after she had first worked out the results mentally.

'2 times 6 is 12,
3 times 6 is 18,
4 times 6 is 24,
5 times 6 is 30,
That's four (combinations).
six and nine is 15,
six and six and nine is 21,
six and six and six and nine is 27.
That's another three. That's seven so far.
2 times 9 is 18,
3 times 9 is 27,
That's another two. That's nine now.
2 nines and six is 24.
That's ten.'

2.94 After being asked by the tester whether there were any more the pupil said, 'Yes, one: two nines and two sixes. That's eleven (combinations)'. Asked if she had found all the lengths the pupil said, 'Yes. I've got all the six times. I've got all the nine times. I've got all the mixed numbers. There are no more but I think I ought to be allowed to use 6m and 9m on their own.'

2.95 Another pupil worked silently, while recording results on the paper provided:

6 m → 12 m → 18 m → 24 m → 30 m
9 m → 18 m → 27 m

15 m   9 + 6   21 m   9 + 6 + 6   24 m   9 + 9 + 6
27 m   9 + 6 + 6 + 6   9 + 9 + 6 + 6 → 30 m.

Having recorded all the combinations the pupil said, 'All the combinations have been used.'

2.96 One tester reported on a pupil who recorded combinations apparently unsystematically but afterwards summarised them succinctly as: 'All the sixes; all the nines; and all the mixed numbers. There are no more.'

2.97 Other pupils were unable to provide adequate reasons for supporting their view that there were no more combinations;

> 'I've found them all. That's all I can think of.'
> 'I think anything else would go over 30.'

2.98 Some pupils appeared not to understand what was required even when their comprehension of the vocabulary had been probed and the rules of the task demonstrated with the number rods. One pupil placed all the rods end to end to make one long train; another was able to make combinations with two rods only.

2.99 For some pupils the task may have been one of perseverance rather than of problem solving, for they appeared bored after providing a few combinations and gladly answered 'No' when the tester asked if there were any more.

2.100 Not all the pupils found the task acceptable mathematically. One pupil's response on being presented with the problem was:

> 'Is it 4? I am not very good at trick questions, I like real sums.'

Factors

2.101 Pupils were provided with some plastic tiles and asked to make rectangles with them, each rectangle to consist of 12 tiles. The purpose of the task was to establish that with 12 tiles only rectangles with sides which were factors of 12 could be constructed. First, the tester demonstrated the task by constructing a rectangle with 3 tiles across and 4 tiles down, then the pupils were asked to make one with a different shape. Without assistance, over 90 per cent of the pupils did this and 65 per cent then constructed other rectangles. (see Table 2.10).

2.102 Nearly all the pupils interpreted the task as requiring the tiles to cover the rectangular area completely.. One pupil asked 'Do they have to be joined together?' and then produced an outline shape:

2.103 In order to focus on the factors of 12 it was necessary to consider rectangles of the same shape but different orientation as equivalent, so pupils who made both rectangles in such pairs were asked to say what was similar about them. Most often the response was that they were 'the same but a different way', and a number of pupils referred turning one rectangle round to make it the same as the other. A few used the term 'rotation' and one said 'that is horizontal and the other vertical'. One pupil preferred a more graphic illustration:

> 'They are exactly the same but they have been knocked down, (pointing to a cupboard in the room) as though that cupboard had been knocked down on its side.'

2.104 Finally, pupils were asked to explain why no more rectangles could be made and 35 per cent gave an acceptable reply without aid. The explanations were given in a variety of forms and a few were able to use the term 'factor' (eg. 'I've used all the factors of 12'). Other examples of explanations given:

'These are the only numbers that go into 12.'
'I can only use 1, 2, 3, 4, 6 and 12. These are parts of the 12 times table.'
'Because nothing else goes into 12 equally.'
'You couldn't have one 5 tall because it doesn't go into 12 an equal number of times.'

Table 2.10 *Topic on factors: results (1978)*

	% Unaided success	% Aided success
1. Tester asks pupil to tip out tiles and count out 12. Tester arranges these 12 tiles into a rectangle in front of pupil: 3 across and 4 down. 'The outline of these tiles is a rectangle. Count out another 12 tiles and make a rectangle with a different shape.'	92	95
2. Tester repeats above question until pupil can make no more rectangles.	63	70
3. If pupil has given, 4 x 3 and 3 x 4, tester asks: 'What's similar about these shapes?'	71	75
4. Tester sets out the tiles in the following manner:		

1 x 12   2 x 6   3 x 4

'Explain how you know there are no more different rectangles.'

	34	40

Attribute cards

2.105 The ability to sort objects into classes according to their attributes is an important feature of logical development. This topic was based on the type of materials used in schools to give pupils experience of such tasks.

2.106 The materials used were eight cards about 6cm square, each with a pattern having 3 shape attributes (square, circle, triangle) and each attribute having one of two values (dotted or plain outline). These patterns are shown in Fig 2.20.

Figure 2.20 *Attribute cards*

2.107 The tester began the interview by saying
'I'm going to sort these cards into 2 sets using a rule.'
The cards were sorted into dotted and plain outline circles and the pupil was then asked:
'What was my rule?'

2.108 Approximately 45 per cent of the pupils gave a satisfactory response without assistance. A number of pupils were uncertain about what they were required to do, and after clarification of the task, a further 30 per cent were able to give the rule used. (See Table 2.11 for exact results.)

2.109 The cards were than collected into one pile and the tester asked the pupil to 'think of a different rule and sort the cards out. What was your rule? Almost 90 per cent of the pupils did this successfully without help. A second sorting, using another rule, was achieved by about 10 per cent fewer pupils than were able to provide one rule. The tester now pointed out the three attributes of each pattern and then placed the card with three dotted outline shapes before the pupil who was asked to 'put out a card that is different from this in only *one* way.' Chains 6, 7 or 8 cards long can be made in this way. 80 per cent successfully picked out a card differing in only one attribute value from the tester's card without aid. 70 per cent were able to continue the chain of patterns with one attribute value different each time and a further 15 per cent did so after assistance. The final tasks were to make chains of cards each of which differed in two ways from the previous one. Some 70 per cent managed one such chain without help and assistance from the tester enabled over 10 per cent more to do so. Over 80 per cent were able to provide a second example on their own, but prompting only marginally increased the success rate this time.

Table 2.11 *Topic on attribute cards: results (1978)*

	% Unaided success	% Aided success
Sorting		

1.   'I'm going to sort these cards into 2 sets using a rule.'
     Tester sorts shapes into dotted circles and plain circles and asks
     for rule.
	46	75

2.   Tester pushes shapes together.
     'Think of a different rule and sort the cards out. What was
     your rule?'
	89	94

3. Repeat	84	88
Chains		

4.   Tester points out the 3 attributes of the cards and sets out
     card with all shapes dotted.
     'Put out a card that is different from this in only *one* way.'
	81	87

5. 'Continue, making a chain of 8.'	69	82

6.   Tester pushes cards together and sets out all dotted card again.
     'Can you put out a card that is different from this in *two*
     ways? If so, do it.'
	85	88

7. 'Can you put out another card that is different in two ways from the last one?'	67	79
8. If pupil is successful in question 7, tester takes 4 unused cards and asks for a second chain with 2 differences at each step.	82	83

In conclusion

2.110 In the practical testing, pupils' practical skills and their understanding of concepts are assessed. In the 1979 survey the tests involved the understanding and use of measuring instruments such as ruler and protractor; the use of apparatus (for example, a balance and scissors) and a range of 'everyday' materials such as string, paper and pegs to carry out various tasks involving mathematical concepts and activities.

2.111 As in the 1978 survey testers frequently mentioned the relaxed way in which most pupils carried out the tasks, the involvement of the lower ability pupils, and problems with language. In relation to language, some testers reported instances of technical terms 'getting in the way of children's ability to respond' (as one tester put it). Also mentioned were the difficulties many pupils had when they were asked to justify statements or to explain their actions. The geometric shape topic illustrated how graphically pupils can use language to describe their perceptions of a category (rectangles 'lie down'; rectangles are 'flat, long and not very wide'), and yet few could employ definitions consisting of lists of attributes to categorise objects unequivocally.

2.112 The testers provided perceptively detailed critiques of the tests and valuable suggestions for developing the topics. At a debriefing held in London after the survey, they gave their accounts of how the testing had proceeded. They reported having been well received in schools and commented that the use of teachers rather than 'researchers' as testers had been appreciated by the schools involved. In addition, they had enjoyed the opportunity to explore the thinking and strategies of children. That they did so with keen perception and sensitivity is evident in the results reported.

3 Attitudes to mathematics

Background

3.1 The attitude questionnaire that was used in this survey was identical to that which was administered in the 1978 survey. A full description of the questionnaire itself, its development and its statistical reliability can be found in the first primary survey report.

3.2 Briefly, the questionnaire consisted of a set of 42 statements concerning the liking, difficulty and usefulness of mathematics and a list of 34 mathematical topics which pupils rated in terms of liking and difficulty. Pupils were also asked to note if they had not done a particular topic. This gave some indication of the extent to which some topics are taught in the schools, with the caveat that unfamiliarity with a topic name does not necessarily imply unfamiliarity with the topic itself.

The sample 3.3 As in 1978, the number of pupils participating was about 10 per cent of the main sample, but by taking fewer pupils per school more schools took part than in 1978. This procedure produced a sample more representative of the population.

Administration 3.4 Teachers were requested to administer the questionnaire before the written tests so that pupils would not be influenced by their experience with the written test. In Wales, the administration instructions and booklets were provided in both English and Welsh, allowing pupils to respond in their preferred language.

The attitude scales

Comparison with 1978 3.5 In 1978, on the basis of their factor structure, the 42 statements had been divided into three scales: a liking scale (17 statements), a difficulty scale (11 statements) and a utility scale (12 statements). (Responses to two statements were not included in the scores because they were not strongly related to any one of the three factors.) In order to ensure that comparison of results between the two years could be considered valid, the 1979 data were first analysed to investigate whether this internal structure remained constant. The resulting analyses showed a reasonable stability. The 40 statements which composed the three scales correlated with much the same factors as in 1978, and the shifts that did occur were not large enough to question the validity of the scales. Furthermore, when each of the scales was examined for internal consistency, the reliability statistics for the liking and difficulty scales were almost identical to those found in the 1978 survey. The utility scale, which had shown the least reliability in 1978, continued to do so in 1979. Of the three scales, the utility scale was the least robust, possibly because of the lack of variance in responses (ie, the tendency on the part of the pupils to agree that maths is a useful subject).

3.6 Mean scores on the difficulty and utility scales remained relatively stable over the year, showing only a slight rise. As in 1978, the mean utility score was very high. From a possible range of 0 to 24, the mean score was 20.4 (SD 3.2), compared with 20.1 (SD 3.7) in the previous year. The difficulty scale also showed a small and insignificant rise. (The difficulty scale is reversed, so that high scores reflect ease rather than difficulty.) From a possible range of 0 to 22, the mean score was 11.8 (SD 4.9) compared with 11.3 (SD 5.4) in 1978.

3.7 In comparison with the other scales, the rise in the liking scale mean score was statistically significant. From a possible range of 0 to 34, the 21.6 (SD 8.2) mean score was 1.6 higher than that of the previous year. Analysis of the response pattern to individual statements on that scale suggests that the rise can be accounted for largely by a shift from the extremes of certain response categories to an undecided position. That is, a significantly smaller proportion of pupils agreed with negative statements or disagreed with positive statements. These shifts were balanced by increases in the proportion of pupils who ticked the 'Unsure' column. From this evidence, it appears that the increase in the liking score can be accounted for, not by an increase in positive feelings towards mathematics but by a decrease in negative feelings.

3.8 As was the case in 1978, the difficulty and liking scales were closely related, the correlation between them being 0.59. Perhaps more interesting was the finding that utility also was more closely related to liking than it was to difficulty. In fact, when the degree to which pupils liked or disliked mathematics was removed from the analysis, the correlation between the utility and the difficulty scales was minimal (0.11). In contrast, when the degree to which pupils found mathematics easy or difficult was removed, the relationship between utility and liking remained substantive (0.26). This indicates that pupils' perception of mathematics as a useful subject is basically independent of how difficult they find it. Although one cannot deny the effect of difficulty on pupils' attitudes towards mathematics, it is apparent from this analysis that the extent to which they perceive it as a useful subject exerts a strong influence on their tendency to find it an enjoyable one, and vice versa.

Sex differences

3.9 As in 1978 the mean scores of boys and girls on the three scales were similar (within 0.7 points of each other). However, a comparison of their responses to individual statements on the scales showed interesting dissimilarities. These differences were most apparent in the responses to those statements which comprised the difficulty scale, and, specifically, in the responses to those statements which reflected a confidence in mathematical ability. For example, significantly more boys than girls believed that they usually understood a new mathematical idea quickly, that they were usually correct in their work and that maths was one of their better subjects. In contrast, at least 9 per cent more girls than boys (a statistically significant difference) confirmed that they often got into difficulty with maths and were surprised when they suceeded. It is interesting to note that these significant differences between the sexes generally occurred in response to statements reflecting a judgement of personal ability rather than those referring to the difficulty of the subject itself. More objective statements elicited little difference between the sexes. It appears that, at 11 years old, boys already indicate greater self-confidence than girls in mathematics.

*M. Preece (1979). Mathematics: the unpredictability of girls? Mathematics Teaching 87, 27-29.

3.10 This finding is in general accord with other studies of older pupils. For example, in a study of second year secondary pupils in England, Preece* found

**Achievement and participation of women in mathematics: an overview. (1980) Education Commission of the States.*

that boys exhibited a greater degree of self-confidence and a greater expectation of success than girls. Similarly, in a United States survey of 13 year olds** 9 per cent more boys than girls responded positively to a statement expressing personal confidence in their mathematical ability.

3.11 In contrast, there were few differences between boys and girls in their reaction to statements concerning the enjoyment of mathematics. Only 2 of the 17 statements that comprised the liking scale elicited any significant difference in response. In both cases more girls than boys expressed positive feeling. Despite their relative lack of self-confidence it appears that the girls generally tended to enjoy mathematics to the same extent as boys, with more girls looking forward to their mathematics lessons.

3.12 Possibly because of the high positive response to statements concerning the usefulness of mathematics, little difference was found between boys and girls on this scale. Both sexes appeared to recognise the utility of mathematics, with girls showing somewhat more uncertainty than boys.

* Educational Commission of the States, *op. cit.*

** Preece, *op. cit.*

3.13 Again, these results support the findings of other studies. 13 year old boys and girls in the United States* differed little in their response to statements concerning the usefulness and enjoyment of maths. In an English study of the same age group, Preece** found that while both boys and girls thought mathematics important, girls claimed a greater intrinsic interest in the subject. The extent of the difference between the sexes in their attitude towards mathematics appears to be most closely allied to its perceived difficulty and pupils' self-confidence. The divergence has been clearly documented in surveys of older pupils and the results of this survey suggest it is already present in this age group.

Topics

3.14 Two identical lists of 34 topics were presented for rating in terms of liking and difficulty. In each case there was a column for those pupils who were unsure of their feelings and a column which pupils were asked to tick if they believed that they had not done the topic.

Comparison with 1978 results

3.15 The percentage of pupils ticking the 'Not done' column increased by at least 6 per cent in the case of 'geometry', 'prime numbers', 'number bases' and 'algebra'. 9 per cent more pupils asserted that they had not done percentages in mathematics lessons, and the number of pupils who did not recognise volume rose from 34 to 42 per cent. Apart from this increase in the number of pupils who stated that they had not done certain topics, few other significant changes occurred. The only noteworthy topic is decimals. Here, 7 per cent more pupils stated that they liked working in decimals, while 6 per cent fewer pupils found them difficult.

Sex differences

3.16 As in 1978, statistically significant differences occurred mainly in the sub-categories involving measures and were usually accounted for by a larger proportion of boys liking a topic or finding it easy. In these cases, girls were more apt to tick the 'Not sure' column than to declare that they disliked a topic or found it difficult. The exception to this rule was in response to the general term,

'Measuring'. Although the majority of pupils indicated that they liked measuring and found it easy, there were significantly more dissenters among the girls than the boys. Boys also tended to like spatial topics, such as geometry and angles, more than girls.

3.17 In the numerical topics significant differences occurred in the 'Not sure' column, more girls than boys being undecided about their feelings towards these topics. Multiplication tables, alone in a list of topic names, elicited more positive response from girls than boys. Table 3.1 presents results for the topics in which the difference in response between boys and girls is significant.

Table 3.1 *Sex differences in response to the topic names*

		*Percentage of Responses				Percentage of Responses			
		Like	Unsure	Dislike	Not Done	Easy	Unsure	Hard	Not Done
Geometry	B	29	15	10	46	21	18	14	46
	G	22	22	8	48	15	27	11	48
Angles	B	46	20	28	6				
	G	39	25	30	7				
Measuring	B	72	14	12	2	72	15	10	4
	G	60	16	21	3	61	20	16	3
Weighing	B					53	25	14	9
	G					42	35	19	4
Time	B	75	11	10	3	76	13	7	4
	G	64	17	17	3	68	20	9	3
Length	B	67	18	13	3	63	17	18	4
	G	54	27	16	3	55	22	21	2
Volume	B					16	19	20	44
	G					13	29	18	40
Factors	B	32	19	19	30				
	G	25	27	18	31				
Averages	B					34	21	19	26
	G					35	28	14	24
Number Patterns	B					47	18	10	25
	G					48	27	7	18
Multiplication Tables	B	63	14	20	2				
	G	73	13	13	2				

The boxes indicate that the proportions within are significantly different.

* In each case the percentage figure is rounded to the nearest whole number.

Pupils' comments

3.18 As a final task, pupils were asked to give their opinion of the questionnaire. Approximately 10 per cent took this opportunity to comment. Many obviously enjoyed the fact that their views were regarded as important. The questions provided them with the opportunity to reflect on a situation which they had normally taken as 'given'. As a result, they appeared to have given the questionnaire careful consideration. For example, pupils wrote:

'I thought the questions brought out answers which I wouldn't have spoken aloud about. The paper was interesting and made you think about maths. I didn't realise I'd learned so much about maths.'

'I think this questionnaire is very useful for scientists who are finding out about maths. I liked it very much because I have never actually realised what I did like and what I did not like.'

'It is an interesting test. The first time I have been asked "How do I like mathematics?"'

3.19 In some cases, pupils found the questionnaire a bit disconcerting, as seen in the following responses.

'I think that the questionnaire is alright but some of it is confusing to me, and I don't know if I have done some or not done some.'

'I think that the questions are interesting but a bit personal, but I liked answering them. I also found some of them quite amusing.'

3.20 For some pupils, the opportunity to give their opinions freely and anonymously was an enjoyable experience. One pupil, for example, commented that he liked the chance to say 'What I thought of maths without them knowing who I was.'

Another commented: 'I think it was good. I like the way we were allowed to say what we like about maths. If we like it or don't like it, and in my case I don't.'

3.21 Some pupils regarded the questionnaire in a larger context. One pupil wrote:

'I think it is good because eventually all school children in Wales and England will know how many children like maths and decide to stop pretending they don't like maths.'

Others were less sanguine, such as the pupil who wrote:

'On the whole, I do not think much will come of this, as most people do not like maths. Because of this the standard of mathematics has fallen.'

Finally, there were the dissenters. They took the opportunity to express their dissatisfaction with the enterprise, gently:

'I think this was worth doing, but I would rather have been doing English.'

and more decisively:

'I found it rather interesting but most of the subjects do not apply to me because I want to be a magician, so I find them pointless.'

Conclusions

3.22 Although the scales gave a measure of pupils' general feelings towards mathematics, pupils' responses to particular topics gave a clearer indication of what, for them, mathematics consists of. For instance, less than 50 per cent of the pupils recognised such terms as 'tessellations' and 'algebra', whereas over 90 per cent were able to comment on 'graphs' and 'decimals' in addition to the more basic number and practical topics that form the curriculum in primary schools.

3.23 It must be conceded that some terms may not have been recognised by pupils. This is apparent from teachers' ratings of the appropriateness of the same topics. For example, whereas 38 per cent of the pupils indicated that they had not done 'symmetry', only 6 per cent of teachers replied that they considered the topic to be inappropriate.

3.24 Although girls' and boys' total scores on the three scales were similar, disparities arose when responses to individual statements were compared. Girls appeared to feel less confident in their mathematical ability, and yet indicated the same degree of positive feelings toward the subject as boys did. Their preferences became clearer in response to individual topics. Although generally tending to be less sure of their feelings than boys, fewer girls like the more practical topics or found them easy.

4 The written tests: sub-category scores and background variables

The 1979 survey tests

4.1 The written tests used for the 1979 survey were identical to those used in 1978, apart from small typographical improvements. The 13 sub-categories of primary school mathematics which were assessed, and the number of items which were used are given in Table 4.1

Table 4.1 *Number of items used within each sub-category in the 1979 primary survey*

Main content category	Sub-category	Number of items
Geometry	Lines, angles and shapes	48
	Symmetry, transformations, coordinates	41
Measures	Money, time, mass, temperature	57
	Length, area, volume and capacity	45
Number	Concepts (whole numbers)	63
	Concepts (decimals and fractions)	61
	Computation (whole numbers and decimals)	61
	Computation (fractions)	54
	Applications of number	57
	Rate and ratio	33
Algebra	Generalised arithmetic	62
	Sets and relations	27
Probability and statistics	Probability and data representation	38

4.2 The aim of the testing design, described fully in *Primary survey report No. 1*, was to provide a mean score and distribution of scores for each of the 13 sub-categories. Each test contained items from three of the sub-categories, at least one of which was from a content area likely to be familiar to all pupils, namely number or measures. Within each of the three clearly indicated sections, items were placed in approximate order of increasing difficulty. The six parts of each sub-category were placed twice in the first section, twice in the second and twice in the third section of the different tests in which they appeared. Table 4.2 shows the sub-categories assessed in each of the 26 tests; for example test 26 contains items from: symmetry, transformations and coordinates; computation, whole numbers and decimals and generalised arithmetic.

Table 4.2 *Summary of testing design showing the sub-categories covered in each test*

	Test No	01	02	03	04	05	06	07	08	09	10	11	12	13	14	15	16	17	18	19	20	21	22	23	24	25	26
Geometry	P Lines, angles and shapes			P1				P2					P3				P4						P5		P6		
	B Symmetry, transformations, co-ordinates			B1			B2						B3					B4			B5						B6
Measures	R Money, time, mass, temperature	R1				R2					R3					R4		R5					R6				
	D Length, area, volume, capacity			D1			D2				D3			D4				D5						D6			
Number	E Concepts (whole number)		E1						E2					E3					E4		E5					E6	
	F Concepts (decimals and fractions)		F1					F2		F3				F4						F5		F6					
	G Computation (whole numbers and decimals)		G1						G2						G3					G4				G5			G6
	H Computation: fractions				H1					H2					H3		H4			H5						H6	
	J Applications of number				J1				J2			J3			J4				J5						J6		
	K Ratio and rate				K1					K2			K3						K4				K5	K6			
Algebra	M Generalised arithmetic	M1				M2						M3				M4					M5						M6
	N Sets and relations	N1					N2					N3					N4					N5				N6	
Probability and Statistics	L Probability and data representation					L1		L2			L3					L4						L5			L6		

4.3 In all, 14,522 pupils completed written tests, giving an effective sample size of approximately 1,800 pupils for each sub-category once the data had been edited and weighted to provide representative proportions of pupils in each stratum of the sampling design. (See Appendix 1 for a detailed account of the sample.)

The sub-category scores 4.4 The typographical improvements made to the items for the 1979 tests did not significantly affect the proportion of pupils answering correctly, although changes did arise in a number of cases where items were marked differently. Occasionally, where two parts of an item had been separately marked in 1978, they were combined and treated as one item in 1979 and some items which had been treated as single responses in 1978 were split into their component parts in 1979. These changes were made in order to release more information, or more easily interpreted information, about the pupils' responses to the items concerned. Inevitably the changes influenced the percentage of items answered correctly by the pupils since the effect was to replace some single hard items with a number of easier ones and vice versa. The procedure used to obtain sub-category scores for the 1978 data (page 22 of *Primary survey report No. 1*) was to express each pupil's score as a percentage of the maximum possible on the part he or she attempted and average the data from the six sub-category parts. Clearly if the same approach were adopted for the data from the 1979 survey different scores would be reported in some sub-categories because the marking of some items had been changed rather than because of any change in performance for the sub-category as a whole.

4.5 What was required therefore was to make allowance for the changed average difficulty of each test or sub-category as a whole. The use of scaled scores is one way in which this can be done and an account of the method used for this purpose is given in Appendix 3.

Figure 4.1 *The relationship between the scaled scores and the percentage of items which would be answered correctly if all the items in the sub-category were used as a single test.*

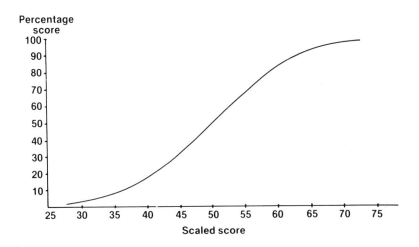

4.6 Figure 4.1 shows the relationship between the scaled scores reported in this chapter and the more familiar way of expressing test scores as a percentage of correct responses. The figure provides an approximate conversion of the scaled scores into their equivalents in terms of the percentage of items in the sub-category which would be answered correctly if all the items were used as a single test. Thus a mean scaled score of 50 implies that 50 per cent of the items would be answered correctly by the average pupil. A mean scaled score of 45 implies that just over 30 per cent of the items would be answered correctly by the average pupil, a mean scaled score of 60 that just under 85 per cent of the items would be answered correctly by such a pupil, and so on. In addition it can be seen from Figure 4.1 that the majority of scaled scores are likely to lie in the range from 30 to 70 scaled units since this band covers the range of 5 to 95 per cent of items answered correctly.

The 1978 and 1979 results compared

4.7 Northern Ireland did not participate in the 1978 primary mathematics survey although it has been involved in all subsequent APU work. Thus in order to compare like with like, the comparisons of performance between the two years which are reported in this section use only the data gathered in England and Wales in 1979. The combined results for England, Wales and Northern Ireland are also given to facilitate year by year comparisons in later reports.

4.8 The change in mean score between the two years is only statistically significant* in two sub-categories, namely computation (whole numbers and decimals) and computation (fractions). In these two sub-categories there has been a rise in performance, there has been no statistically significant fall in performance in any sub-category between 1978 and 1979.

*Whenever the words "significant" or "statistically significant" are used in this chapter they refer to statistical significance at the 5 per cent level. Note that this does not necessarily imply *educational* significance (see Appendix 2).

4.9 In the two sub-categories where there was a statistically significant rise in mean scaled score between 1978 and 1979 there was no evidence that the changes applied to any particular group of items or area of content. However a wider range of errors was coded than in 1978 making it possible to give more coherent interpretations of pupils' performance in a number of areas of mathematics. Some examples of these appear in Chapter 5.

The background variables

4.10 In this section five characteristics of the schools in the sample are used to describe the pattern of performance. These are:

1. Size of the 10-plus age group
2. Pupil/teacher ratio
3. Percentage of pupils taking free school meals
4. Location in a metropolitan or non-metropolitan authority
5. Region of the country

Separate data for boys and girls are also reported.

4.11 For each background variable a comparison has been made between the scores obtained in 1978 and 1979. As explained in paragraph 4.7 these comparisons are only valid for England and Wales since Northern Ireland did not participate in the first primary mathematics survey. However it can be seen from Table 4.3 that the inclusion of the Northern Ireland pupils in the mean scaled scores has little effect and so for brevity only the data for the whole sample in 1979 are given in Tables 4.4 to 4.9. Nonetheless references in the text to differences between performance in the two years refer only to pupils in England and Wales.

Table 4.3 *Mean and standard deviation* of the scaled scores in each sub-category in 1978 and 1979.*

	England, Wales & NI 1979		England & Wales 1979		England & Wales 1978	
	Mean	SD	Mean	SD	Mean	SD
Lines, angles and shapes	50.4	6.6	50.4	6.6	50.2	6.5
Symmetry, transformation and coordinates	50.5	6.0	50.5	6.0	50.7	6.0
Money, time, weight and temperature	53.3	7.2	53.2	7.2	53.1	7.3
Length, area, volume and capacity	51.8	6.7	51.7	6.7	51.3	6.8
Concepts (whole numbers)	53.8	7.0	53.7	7.0	53.5	7.1
Concepts (fractions and decimals)	49.7	8.3	49.6	8.3	49.3	8.4
Computation (whole numbers and decimals)	52.3	7.3	52.2	7.3	51.4	7.0
Computation (fractions)	45.2	8.1	45.0	8.1	44.3	7.9
Applications of number	51.7	7.5	51.6	7.5	51.5	7.6
Rate and ratio	47.3	7.2	47.2	7.2	46.8	7.2
Generalised arithmetic	45.8	6.9	45.7	6.9	45.6	6.7
Sets and relations	50.1	7.0	50.1	7.0	50.3	7.0
Probability and data representation	50.1	6.5	50.0	6.5	49.8	6.7

* *Standard deviation is a measure of the dispersion of the scores: the higher the standard deviation the more the scores are spread out about the mean.*

4.12 The differences between the mean scaled scores obtained by the pupils in each grouping of the background variables and the mean scaled score obtained for all the pupils who took the sub-category in 1979 are shown in graphical form in Figure 4.2 to 4.7. In each case an indication is given of confidence limits, that is, the range within which these differences are most likely to lie for the total population. For example, in Figure 4.2, the mean difference score in the lines, angles and shapes sub-category for the sample in schools with less than 31 pupils in the 10-plus age group is shown +0.8 (from Tables 4.3 and 4.4: 51.2 - 50.4 = 0.8) while countrywide for all pupils in schools with under 31 pupils in the 10-plus age group the mean score is most likely to lie between 0 and + 1.6.

4.13 It is useful as a rule of thumb to note those occasions where there is only a small overlap, or none at all, between two sets of confidence limits. In these cases the discrepancy between the two mean scores concerned is so large that it is unlikely to have arisen solely from sampling fluctuations and is thus likely to be significant in the statistical sense (see Appendix 2).

4.14 It is important to interpret the discrepancies in mean score between the groupings of the background variables in the light of the much larger differences occurring between pupils within the groupings. For example, despite the association between performance and the affluence of schools' catchment areas there are still many pupils attending schools in areas of low affluence whose performance would be high amongst any group of 11 year olds.

4.15 Another proviso affecting the data on the background variables must also be mentioned. The variables are not all independent and although comment is made concerning some of the major interactions between them, no detailed analysis of the effects of these interactions is reported here. Work is continuing on the use of more explanatory analyses and until these are carried out the relationships between the background variables and performance reported here must be interpreted with care. Finally, as with all studies which use correlational methods a causal relationship cannot be assumed simply because a strong association is reported between any particular background variable and performance. For example, other researchers have reported a substantial correlation between the attitudes of parents to school and the school performance of their children. However, this does not imply that positive parental attitudes are a direct cause of their children's good performance. Indeed it might equally well be that having successful children promotes healthy parental attitudes towards school or that both the parents' attitudes and child's performance depend upon some common factor underlying both variables.

Size of the 10-plus age group

* References to maintained schools are used in the English sense: All schools in Northern Ireland involved in the survey, whether controlled, maintained or voluntary, would have been categorised as maintained had they been in England.

4.16 This analysis relates only to schools in the maintained sector.* Table 4.4 and Figure 4.2 show the results obtained for each sub-category by pupils in schools assigned to one of four groups on the basis of the size of their 10-plus age group.

Group	Size of 10-plus age group	Percentage of maintained school sample
1	Over 90 pupils	24
2	61 to 90 pupils	32
3	31 to 60 pupils	30
4	less than 31 pupils	14

4.17 It can be seen that the mean scaled scores of pupils in the schools in group 4 are frequently higher than those of pupils in the other three groups. The difference between groups 4 and 3 is statistically significant in two sub-categories, namely money, time, weight and temperature, and rate and ratio. The difference between groups 4 and 2 is statistically significant in five sub-categories: the two geometry ones, the two measures ones and rate and ratio. The difference between groups 4 and 1 is also statistically significant in five sub-categories: the two measures ones, lines, angles and shapes, rate and ratio, and computation (whole numbers and decimals). None of the differences between groups 1, 2 and 3 is statistically significant, nor are those between group 4 and the others in the number concepts sub-categories, where, against the general pattern, pupils in the group 4 schools do not obtain the highest mean scores. In *Primary survey report No. 1*, performance was described against the variable of school size, not size of age group.

Table 4.4 *Mean scaled scores for each sub-category by size of 10-plus age group.*

	England, Wales & N.I. 1979				England & Wales 1978			
	>90	61-90	31-60	<31	>90	61-90	31-60	<31
Group	1	2	3	4	1	2	3	4
Lines, angles and shapes	50.0	50.1	50.5	51.2	49.8	49.7	50.1	51.3
Symmetry, transformation and coordinates	50.3	49.9	50.5	50.9	50.2	50.4	50.2	52.3
Money, time, weight and temperature	52.8	52.9	53.1	54.1	52.6	53.0	53.1	53.5
Length, area, volume and capacity	51.2	51.3	52.0	52.5	51.3	50.6	51.1	52.6
Concepts (whole numbers)	53.2	53.9	53.8	53.5	52.8	52.9	53.5	54.7
Concepts (fractions and decimals)	49.0	49.1	49.9	49.1	48.4	48.4	49.5	50.3
Computation (whole numbers and decimals)	51.6	52.0	52.4	52.7	50.6	51.2	51.2	52.2
Computation (fractions)	45.0	44.8	44.8	45.7	43.7	43.6	44.1	45.2
Applications of number	51.1	51.5	51.6	52.0	50.8	50.8	51.5	52.5
Rate and ratio	46.5	47.0	47.1	48.4	46.4	46.1	46.8	47.6
Generalised arithmetic	45.3	45.6	45.5	46.0	45.3	44.9	45.7	46.4
Sets and relations	49.7	49.8	50.1	50.5	49.9	49.6	50.1	51.1
Probability and data representation	49.6	49.8	49.9	50.4	49.1	49.3	50.0	50.1

4.18 Further analyses of the structure of the performance differences related to size of age group indicate that much of them can be explained in terms of school location. The proportion of the schools in group 4 which are located in non-metropolitan authorities is considerably higher than for the other groups and there is little relationship between size of age group and performance once this effect is allowed for. Nonetheless it is of interest to note that the scores of pupils from schools with less than 31 pupils in the age group which have relatively less affluent catchment areas (as measured by the proportion of pupils taking free school meals) are not generally as low as those of pupils from similarly less affluent schools where the 10-plus age group is larger.

Figure 4.2 *Differences from each sub-category's overall mean scaled score for size of 10-plus age group.*

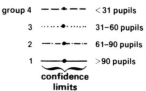

Pupil/teacher ratio   4.19 This analysis relates only to schools in the maintained sector in England and Wales (data on pupil/teacher ratio were not available for Northern Ireland). The sample schools were placed in four groups by the number of pupils per teacher as follows:

Group	Pupils per teacher	Percentage of maintained school sample in England and Wales
1	Less than 20	9
2	20 to 24.9	44
3	25 to 27.4	33
4	27.5 and above	14

Head teachers and part-time teachers are included in this analysis.

Table 4.5 *Mean scaled scores for each sub-category by pupil/teacher ratio.*

	England & Wales 1979				England & Wales 1978			
	<20	20-24.9	25-27.4	≥27.5	<20	20-24.9	25-27.4	≥27.5
Group	1	2	3	4	1	2	3	4
Lines, angles and shapes	48.7	50.0	50.6	51.5	48.5	49.5	50.5	50.8
Symmetry, transformation and coordinates	48.5	50.2	50.8	50.8	50.5	49.9	50.7	51.4
Money, time, weight and temperature	50.8	53.0	53.4	53.5	50.7	52.2	53.5	54.1
Length, area, volume and capacity	49.7	51.0	52.3	52.7	49.7	50.7	51.6	52.0
Concepts (whole numbers)	51.0	53.4	54.1	54.1	52.1	52.6	53.8	54.2
Concepts (fractions and decimals)	46.1	48.4	50.4	50.8	46.7	47.9	50.1	49.8
Computation (whole numbers and decimals)	49.7	51.4	52.7	53.1	50.0	50.4	52.0	52.0
Computation (fractions)	41.6	44.3	45.7	46.2	43.2	42.8	42.3	44.5
Applications of number	49.5	50.9	51.9	52.8	49.3	50.6	51.7	52.1
Rate and ratio	45.4	46.6	47.3	48.7	45.4	46.0	47.2	47.1
Generalised arithmetic	43.5	45.3	45.9	46.0	44.7	44.7	45.7	46.5
Sets and relations	49.1	49.6	50.5	50.4	49.2	49.7	50.4	50.5
Probability and data representation	48.2	49.5	50.3	50.2	47.2	48.8	49.8	51.1

Figure 4.3 *Differences from each sub-category's overall mean scaled score for pupil/teacher ratio.*

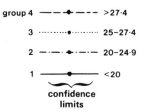

group 4 — — ◆ — — >27·4

3 ·········●········· 25–27·4

2 —·—◆—·— 20–24·9

1 ——●—— <20

confidence limits

4.20 It can be seen from Table 4.5 and Figure 4.3 that the pattern of performance with pupil/teacher ratio is similar to that obtained in the 1978 survey. In 1979 the difference between groups 1 and 2 is significant in eleven of the sub-categories (the exceptions are lines, angles and shapes; and sets and relations) rather than two. The difference between groups 2 and 3 is significant in ten of the sub-categories, and the difference between groups 3 and 4 is significant in two sub-categories. As in the 1978 survey, an apparently less favourable pupil/teacher ratio is associated with higher scores on the APU mathematics tests. The differences cannot be explained in terms of the affluence of the schools' catchment areas (as measured by the percentage of pupils taking free meals) although the differences are reduced if allowance is made for this latter variable. Neither do factors relating to school location and size of the 10-plus age group explain the pattern of performance with pupil/teacher ratio.

Table 4.6 *Mean scaled scores for each sub-category by proportion of pupils taking free school meals.*

	England & Wales & NI 1979			England & Wales 1978		
	<16	16-35.9	≥36	<16	16-35.9	≥36
Group	1	2	3	1	2	3
Lines, angles and shapes	51.6	49.7	47.5	51.7	49.7	48.2
Symmetry, transformation and coordinates	51.3	49.8	47.9	51.8	50.3	49.0
Money, time, weight and temperature	54.4	52.3	50.6	54.7	52.7	50.6
Length, area, volume and capacity	52.8	50.9	49.5	52.7	51.1	49.2
Concepts (whole numbers)	54.8	52.6	52.3	54.7	53.2	51.2
Concepts (fractions and decimals)	50.5	48.6	47.4	51.2	48.4	46.7
Computation (whole numbers and decimals)	53.1	51.2	51.0	52.6	50.9	49.5
Computation (fractions)	46.0	44.1	43.3	45.8	43.4	42.2
Applications of number	52.4	50.9	49.8	52.6	51.1	49.3
Rate and ratio	48.2	46.3	45.1	48.0	46.4	44.6
Generalised arithmetic	46.5	45.2	43.0	46.8	45.2	43.8
Sets and relations	51.0	49.5	47.6	51.8	49.5	48.4
Probability and data representation	50.7	49.4	47.7	51.3	49.1	47.5

Figure 4.4 *Differences from each sub-category's overall mean scaled score for the free school meals variable.*

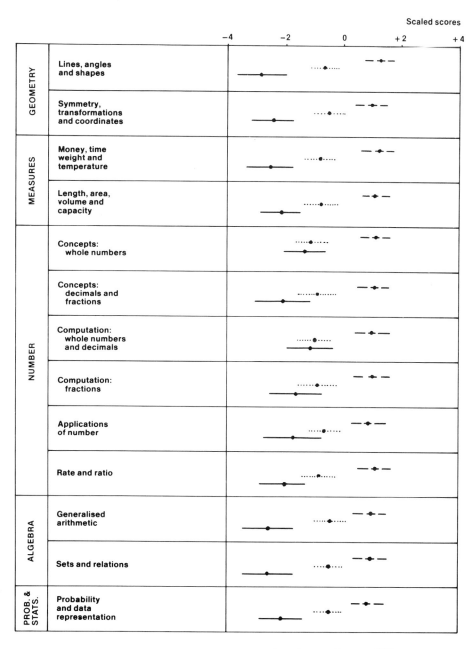

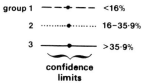

4.21 It must be stressed that the pupil/teacher ratio used in this study cannot be interpreted directly as a measure of size of teaching group because the organisation of schools with the same pupil/teacher ratio can vary markedly with, for example, school size. The primary survey conducted in May 1980 collected data on size of teaching group and this will be reported in the next primary mathematics report.

Percentage of pupils taking free school meals

4.22 This analysis relates only to schools in the maintained sector. In order to obtain an indication of the relative affluence of each school's catchment area this school variable was formed by expressing the number of pupils in a school taking free school lunches on a particular day as a percentage of the total number taking school lunches on that day.

4.23 The schools in the sample were grouped as follows:

Group Taking free school meals Percentage of the maintained school sample

1	less than 16%	50
2	16 to 35.9%	37
3	36% and above	13

4.24 Table 4.6 and Figure 4.4 indicate that, as was the case for the data gathered in 1978, there is a clear association between the affluence of school catchment areas and pupils' performance in 1979. In 1979 all the differences between groups 1 and 2 are significant, while the difference between groups 2 and 3 is not significant in four sub-categories, namely concepts (whole numbers), computation (whole numbers and decimals), computation (fractions) and applications of number.

School location

4.25 The results obtained by pupils in metropolitan and non-metropolitan authorities are shown in Figure 4.5 and Table 4.7. In 1979 the mean performance of pupils from schools in metropolitan authorities is lower, and statistically significantly so, in nine of the sub-categories. The exceptions are concepts (whole numbers), the two computation sub-categories and probability and data representation. As reported in *Primary survey report No. 1* (page 68) there is a greater association between performance in mathematics and the social factors measured by the free school meals variable in metropolitan authorities. However the differences between performance in metropolitan and non-metropolitan authorities remain, even if the effect attributable to the free school meal variable is allowed for.

4.26 The differences in mean score between metropolitan and non-metropolitan authorities cannot be accounted for in terms of the other variables used in the APU work, but more detailed information on school location was collected in 1980 and it should be possible to report more fully on this variable in subsequent reports.

Region

4.27 Figure 4.6 and Table 4.8 show the results obtained for each sub-category by pupils in schools in the five regions.

4.28 There are few statistically significant differences between the three English regions in 1979. In applications of number, pupils in the North and South obtained significantly higher scores than those in the Midlands. In computation (whole numbers and decimals) the scores of pupils in the Midlands were significantly less than those of pupils in the North, and in probability and data representation they were significantly less than those of pupils in the South. There were no significant differences between the performance of pupils in the South and the North.

Figure 4.5 *Differences from each sub-category's overall mean scaled score for school location.*

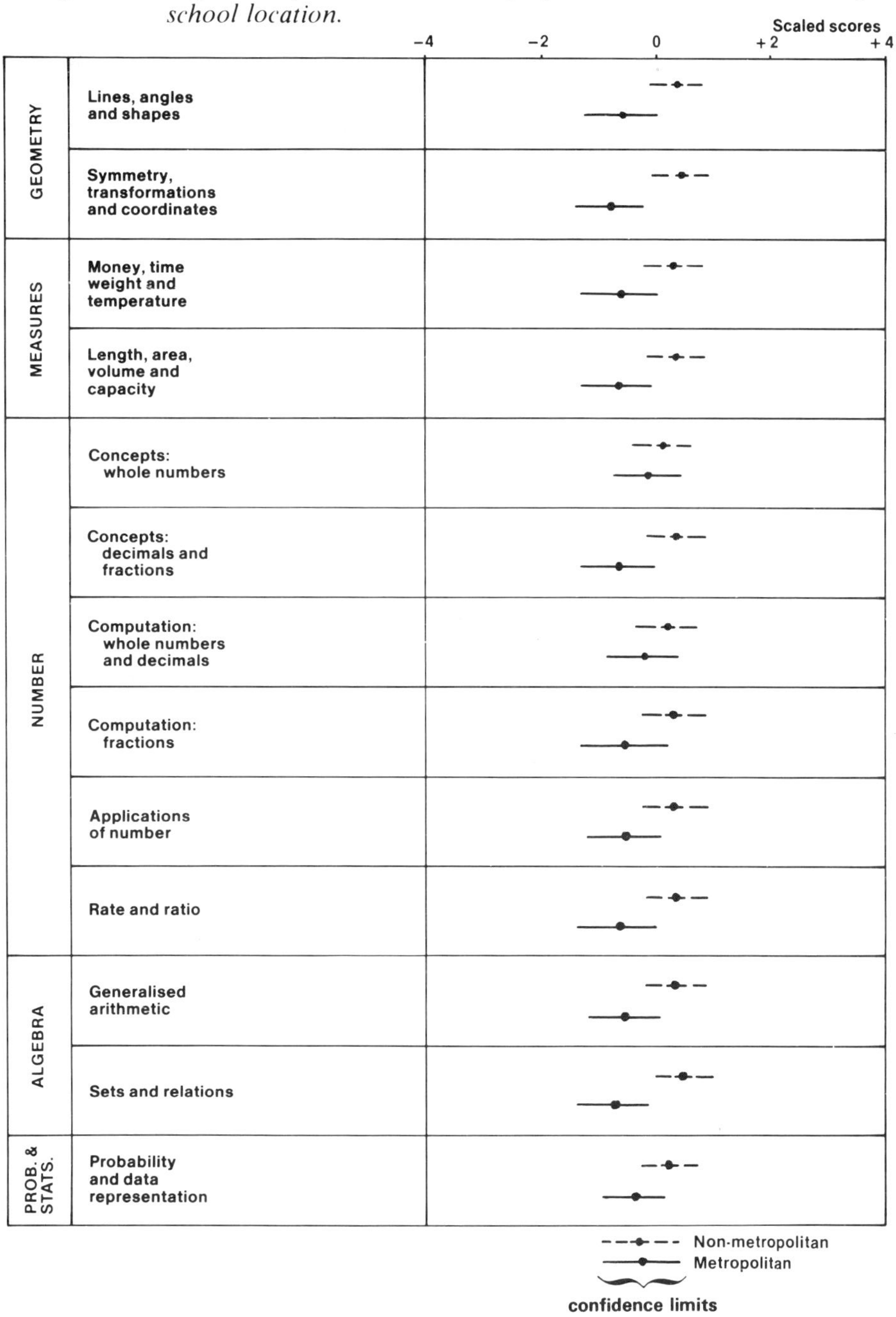

Table 4.7 *Mean scaled scores for each sub-category by school location.*

	England, Wales and NI 1979		England and Wales 1978	
	Met	Non-Met	Met	
Lines, angles and shapes	49.9	50.9	49.5	50.7
Symmetry, transformation and coordinates	49.7	50.9	49.9	51.1
Money, time, weight and temperature	52.7	53.6	52.3	53.6
Length, area, volume and capacity	51.1	52.1	50.5	51.8
Concepts (whole numbers)	53.7	53.9	53.1	53.8
Concepts (fractions and decimals)	49.1	50.1	48.7	49.6
Computation (whole numbers and decimals)	52.1	52.5	50.9	51.6
Computation (fractions)	44.6	45.5	43.3	44.8
Applications of number	51.2	52.0	50.8	51.8
Rate and ratio	46.6	47.7	46.2	47.2
Generalised arithmetic	45.3	46.2	44.9	46.0
Sets and relations	49.4	50.6	49.6	50.7
Probability and data representation	49.7	50.3	49.2	50.1

4.29 Although pupils in Wales again achieved high mean scores in the number sub-categories, in 1979 the difference between Wales and England was statistically significant in only one of them, namely computation with whole numbers and decimals. The mean score for pupils in Wales was significantly lower than that for England in symmetry, transformations and coordinates.

4.30 The most striking aspect of the regional data concerns the performance of the pupils in Northern Ireland. Their mean scores are significantly higher than those of their peers in both England and Wales in twelve of the sub-categories, the only exception being symmetry, transformation and coordinates.

Sex differences

4.31 Figure 4.7 and Table 4.9 show the results obtained by boys and by girls in each sub-category. The boys' mean score is significantly higher in five of the sub-categories in 1979: the two measures ones, concepts (fractions and decimals), applications of number, and rate and ratio.

Figure 4.6   *Differences from each sub-category's overall mean scaled score for region.*

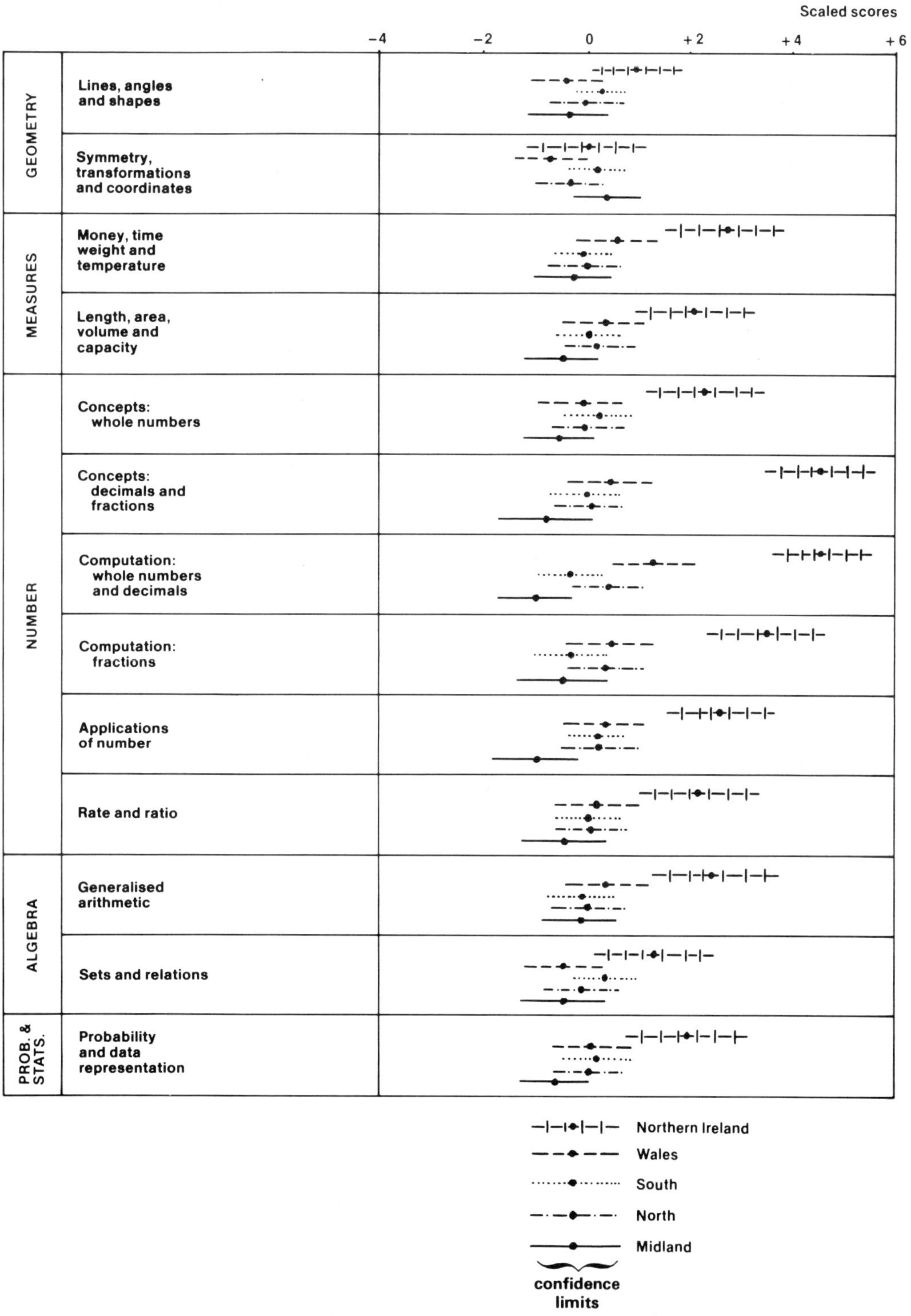

Table 4.8 *Mean scaled scores for each sub-category by region.*

	1979				1978				
	North	Midl	South	Wales	NI	North	Midl	South	Wales
Lines, angles and shapes	50.5	50.1	50.8	50.1	51.5	50.3	49.5	50.6	50.2
Symmetry, transformation and co-ordinates	50.2	50.9	50.6	49.7	50.6	50.3	50.0	51.3	50.6
Money, time, weight and temperature	53.3	53.0	53.2	53.9	55.9	53.5	52.6	53.2	53.4
Length, area, volume and capacity	51.9	51.2	51.8	52.1	53.8	51.4	50.7	51.6	52.0
Concepts (whole numbers)	53.8	53.2	54.0	53.8	56.1	53.8	53.1	53.5	53.6
Concepts (fractions and decimals)	49.7	48.9	49.7	50.2	54.2	49.7	48.3	49.2	51.1
Computation: whole numbers and decimals	52.7	51.3	52.0	53.6	56.9	52.2	49.8	51.3	53.4
Computation (fractions)	45.5	44.7	44.8	45.6	48.6	45.0	43.0	44.2	46.1
Applications of number	51.9	50.7	51.8	52.1	54.3	52.1	50.2	51.6	52.2
Rate and ratio	47.3	46.8	47.3	47.5	49.4	47.3	45.4	47.1	47.8
Generalised arithmetic	45.8	45.7	45.7	46.2	48.3	45.6	45.1	45.8	46.0
Sets and relations	50.1	49.7	50.5	49.7	51.4	50.5	49.8	50.6	49.4
Probability and data representation	50.1	49.4	50.2	50.1	51.9	49.7	49.4	50.0	49.4

Figure 4.7 *Differences from each sub-category's overall mean scaled score for boys and girls.*

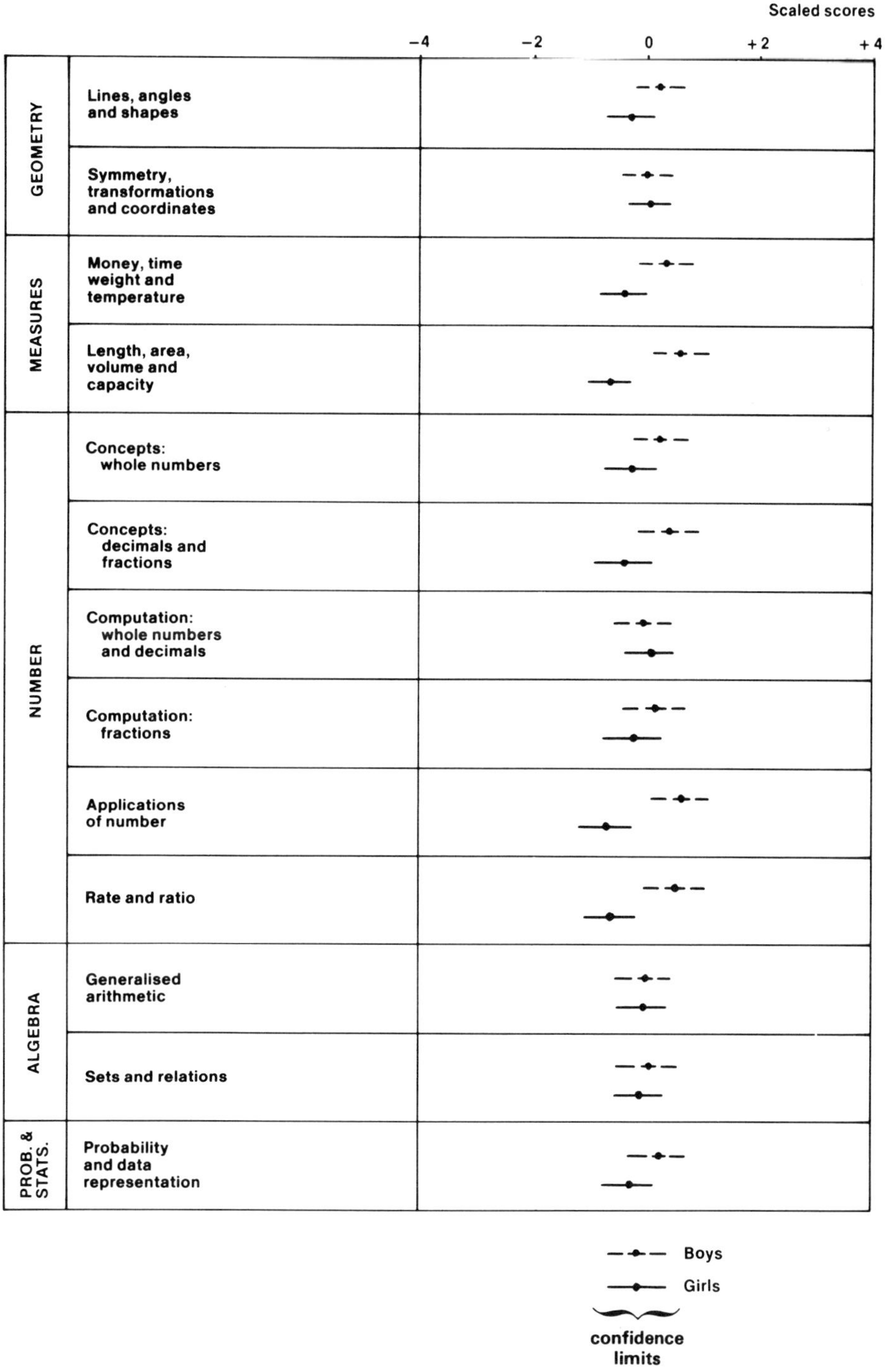

Table 4.9 *Mean scaled scores for each sub-category by sex of pupil.*

	England, Wales & NI 1979		England & Wales 1978	
	Boys	Girls	Boys	Girls
Lines, angles and shapes	50.8	50.3	50.4	50.1
Symmetry, transformations and coordinates	50.5	50.5	50.9	50.5
Money, time, weight and temperature	53.7	52.9	53.4	52.9
Length, area, volume and capacity	52.4	51.1	51.8	50.8
Concepts (whole numbers)	54.1	53.6	53.8	53.2
Concepts (fractions and decimals)	50.1	49.3	49.5	49.0
Computation (whole numbers and decimals	52.3	52.4	50.9	51.9
Computation (fractions)	45.3	45.0	44.5	44.0
Applications of number	52.4	51.0	52.0	50.9
Rate and ratio	47.9	46.7	47.2	46.4
Generalised arithmetic	45.8	45.9	45.5	45.6
Sets and relations	50.3	50.1	50.2	50.5
Probability and data representation	50.3	49.8	49.9	49.6

Summary

4.32 The picture which emerges from the 1979 data when performance on the written tests is studied within the different groupings of the background variables is similar to that obtained in 1978. School location and the relative affluence of schools' catchment areas are associated with performance in general and the boys generally obtained higher mean scores than the girls although the sex difference is only statistically significant in five of the sub-categories. Higher pupil/teacher ratios (ie more pupils per teacher) are again associated with higher mean scores but the pupil/teacher ratio used in this study does not give a direct indication of size of teaching group and should not be interpreted as such. Size of age group is also associated with performance, pupils in the schools with fewer pupils in the 10-plus age group obtaining higher scores than those in schools with middling to large 10-plus age groups. However a high proportion of schools in the smallest 10-plus age group band are located in non-metropolitan authorities so this result is largely a reflection of the data on school location.

4.33 When the results for England and Wales in 1979 are compared with those of 1978, the main point of interest is the statistically significant rise in performance in computation. This rise is equivalent to an increase of about 3 or 4 percentage score points. So if a test of 50 computation items had been given to both the 1978 and 1979 samples, the latter would have got between one and two more items right on average. There has been no statistically significant fall in the performance of the sample as a whole in any sub-category of mathematics between 1978 and 1979.

4.34 The general differences in performance in computation reported in this chapter must be interpreted with circumspection until data from further surveys are available to confirm or deny the existence of any longer-term trend.

5 The written tests: analyses of item clusters

Comparison of 1978 and 1979 results for items

5.1 In those sub-categories where there was a statistically significant difference in mean score between 1978 and 1979, the difference in performance applied generally across the items and was not concentrated in any particular group or area of content. It should be noted that because of the structure of the tests the sample size for each sub-category mean is about three times that for any particular item so that even in those sub-categories where a significant difference exists between mean performance scores there are very few individual items for which the facility values differ significantly. (The facility value of an item is the number of pupils who answered it correctly, expressed as a percentage of the number who took the test containing the item.)

5.2 The overall picture of performance so far as the sub-categories' individual items are concerned is therefore much the same as it was in 1978, as reported in Chapter 3 of *Primary survey report No. 1* and will not be repeated here. Instead, some interpretations of pupils' responses to clusters of items of related content are presented in this chapter. These commentaries are based on the evidence provided by the more detailed coding of responses in the 1979 survey as compared with the one in 1978. Pupils' written responses to individual printed items do not offer such immediate access to their thinking as can be gained in the practical test interviews described in Chapter 2, but when the error analyses for a number of printed items of related content are considered along with the proportions of correct responses and rates of omission, a more detailed picture emerges of the features which affect pupils' performance. The following commentaries have been based on this type of evidence and others will be given in subsequent reports. All the response percentages given are from the 1979 survey.

Line symmetry

B1

Draw the reflection of each shape in the mirror

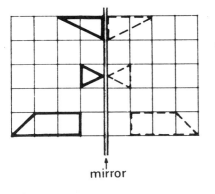

Draw the reflection of each shape in the mirror

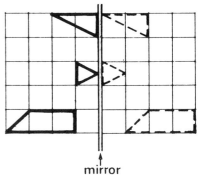

% Correct	% Omitted	% Errors
82	5	4
85	4	4
80	5	3

mirror

5.3 In B1 pupils are asked to draw, on a grid, the reflections of three straight edged closed shapes in a vertical mirror. The results from the three shapes are consistent, 80 to 85 per cent of pupils drawing the correct images. Also consistent is the proportion (about 4 per cent) who placed the reflections at the correct distances from the mirror but did not reverse them (resulting in a translation of the shapes) and the proportion omitting the items (about 5 per cent).

5.4 A simple closed shape is again the object in item B2, but the facility of 14 per cent is well below that of B1. This difference is most likely due to the placing of the mirror diagonally, but there is a further contrasting feature of B2 as compared with B1 in that none of the lines of the object are parallel or perpendicular to the mirror. (The influence of the shape of the object reflected cannot be ruled out but is likely to be minimal in this instance.) The rate of omission (5 per cent) is the same as for B1.

B2 Draw the reflection of the ⌐L shape in the mirror.

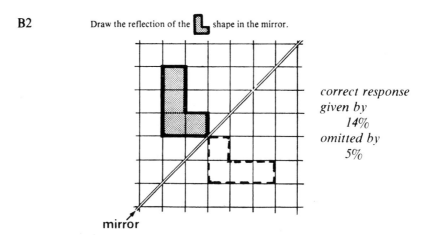

*correct response
given by
14%
omitted by
5%*

mirror

5.5 An additional 14 per cent of the pupils drew a rotation of the object about its point of contact with the mirror lines. They appear to have considered the reflection of the object as a whole but may have started the drawing by translating the lines nearest the mirror across or down the grid instead of reflecting them.

Draw the reflection of the ⌐L shape in the mirror.

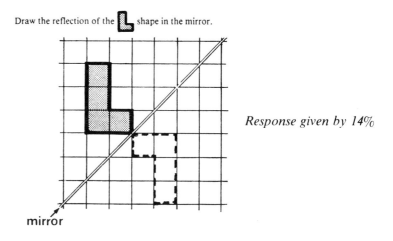

Response given by 14%

mirror

5.6 A further 28 per cent simply drew the image as it would be reversed in a vertical mirror and placed it somewhere on the other side of the mirror line. The figure below is an example of one position of the image in the case of this error.

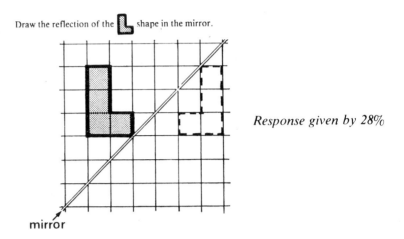

Response given by 28%

5.7 Items B3 and B4 require lines of symmetry to be drawn on plane shapes. In contrast to B1 and B2, the grid is missing, a technical term 'line of symmetry' is introduced and the task is, in essence, the converse of that in B1; namely to draw a mirror line, given object and image. The lower facilities in B3 (50 to 65 per cent) and B4 (20 to 50 per cent) as compared with B1 may be due to any of these changes, but the higher rate of omitting, (consistently 20 to 25 per cent as compared with 5 per cent in B1 and B2), suggests that a principal difficulty is that many pupils are unfamiliar with the term 'line of symmetry'. Placing a diagonal line of symmetry in B3 appears to be a less difficult task than reflecting in a diagonal mirror in B2. On the other hand it may be that the different shapes are responsible for the range of facilities (49 to 66 per cent).

B3

Draw in the line of symmetry on each of these shapes.

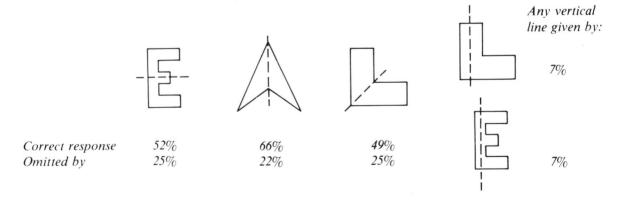

Correct response	*52%*	*66%*	*49%*
Omitted by	*25%*	*22%*	*25%*

5.8 The correct response to the third item in B4 is to draw one vertical line of symmetry and the percentage correct (50 per cent) is about that obtained by pupils in response to the E and L shapes of B3.

5.9 The **B4** item would, however, seem to be more similar to the middle item of B3 which obtained a facility some 15 per cent higher. The difference may be due to the different contexts of the items in some way — the way the instructions are given (draw in 'the line of symmetry' in **B3** and 'all the lines of symmetry' in **B4**), or the influence of the accompanying items in each case.

B4   Draw in all the lines of symmetry on each of these shapes

Correct response   20%   22%   50%
Omitted by   22%   23%   25%

5.10 About 20 per cent of pupils drew only one line of symmetry (horizontal or vertical) on the rectangle and square in spite of the indications in the instruction that there could be more than one. A further proportion of nearly 20 per cent drew both horizontal and vertical lines. This latter strategy produces the correct answer in the case of the rectangle but a deficient answer in the case of the square. If any of these pupils used the same strategy in both items then their responses to the rectangle would be correct fortuitously.

Response analyses for **B4**
Comparison of responses to rectangle and square.

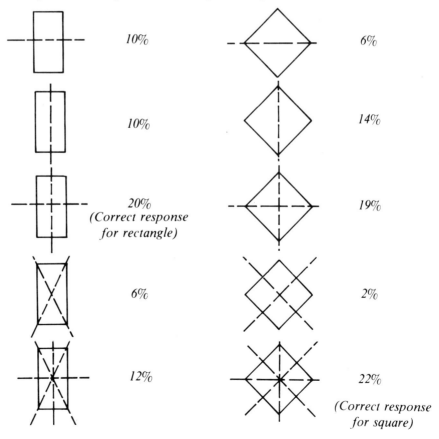

5.11 The evidence of the items in this cluster would indicate that a high proportion of 11 year olds have at least some understanding of line or mirror symmetry. Features of the items in this cluster which affect performance are the orientation of the mirror line and those of the lines of the object and its image in relation to the mirror, the number of lines of symmetry, and technical vocabulary.

Strategies and rules in number

5.12 The 'quantitative' view of children's errors is that they are due to low aptitude or intelligence. In contrast, Piaget[*] has developed the idea that children's mistakes demonstrate that their thinking is organised in accordance with coherent rules or strategies which are qualitatively different from those of adults. Recently it has been suggested[**] that 'children's (arithmetic) errors are often produced by idiosyncratic but meaningful strategies'. It has also been said[†] that children learn to focus on algorithmic procedures rather than when to perform them, that is, they can add or multiply rather better than they know when to add and when to multiply.

5.13 The following analyses look at the evidence in some number items of pupils' use of 'idiosyncratic but meaningful strategies'.

5.14 Items F1 and F2 in the decimals item cluster suggest that when asked to place decimals in order of size, a quarter or more of pupils ignore the decimal points in carrying out the ordinary task. For example, in F1 about 25 per cent ticked the statement '0.56 is greater than 1.3' as correct and about 30 per cent in F2 gave the order of the three numbers in that item, smallest first, as 0.1, 0.07, 0.23.

[*] J Piaget and B Inhelder (1969). *The psychology of the child.* Routledge and Kegan Paul.
[**] H Ginsburg (1977). *Children's arithmetic: the learning process.* Van Nostrand.
J. Brown and R R Burton (1978). *Diagnostic models for procedural bugs in basic mathematical skills.* Cognitive Science 2, 155-192.
[†] J G Green (1978). *Understanding and procedural knowledge in mathematics instruction.* Educational Psychologist 12, 3, 262-283.

F1	Tick the line that is correct				*Ticked by:*
	0.56 is less than 1.3				*56%*
	0.56 is greater than 1.3				*25%*
	0.56 is equal to 1.3				*12%*
					Omitted by:
					6%

F2	Put these decimals in order of size, *smallest* first.	0.07	0.23	0.1	
	Response				*Given by:*
(a)	*Correct*	*0.07*	*0.1*	*0.23*	*23%*
(b)	*Decimal point ignored*	*0.1*	*0.07*	*0.23*	*31%*
(c)	*Reverse of (b)*	*0.23*	*0.07*	*0.1*	*20%*
(d)	*Reverse of (a)*	*0.23*	*0.1*	*0.07*	*2%*
	Omitted				*3%*

F3   Put these decimals in order of size, smallest first.

	0.3	0.1	0.7	0.6	
Response					*Given by:*
Correct	*0.1*	*0.3*	*0.6*	*0.7*	*75%*
Reverse order	*0.7*	*0.6*	*0.3*	*0.1*	*18%*
Omitted					*3%*

5.15 F3 required pupils to carry out a similar ordering task to that in F2, but the numbers involved had only one decimal place. 75 per cent were successful compared with the 23 per cent in F2 who correctly ordered numbers with up to two decimal places.

5.16 About 20 per cent of the pupils gave the correct relative ordering of the numbers in F3 but with the largest placed first. It is possible that all or some of them simply misread or misapplied this detail of the instructions but did understand the principle involved. However, a similar proportion in F2 also seemed to place the largest number first but ignored decimal points; these pupils therefore demonstrated that even if they had misread the instructions they had not understood two place decimal notation.

F4	What number is 10 times 0.5?	*Response:*		*Given by:*
		Correct 5 or 5.0		*38%*
		Others	*0.50*	*14%*
			50	*12%*
			0.05	*2%*
		Omitted by		*14%*
F5	How many times is 0.1 greater than 0.01?	*Correct*	*10*	*47%*
		Others	*100*	*10%*
			1	*8%*
		Omitted by		*13%*

5.17 Items F4 and F5 probed further aspects of place value, the former asking pupils to give the number that is 10 times 0.5. Nearly 30 per cent of the pupils responded by inserting a zero somewhere among the figures; 14 per cent gave the anwer as 0.50, 12 per cent wrote 50 and 2 per cent gave 0.05. It is tempting to speculate that some form of the rules concerning multiplication by 10 (adding a zero; moving the decimal point) was being operated here by pupils who made these errors.

5.18 The errors most frequently made in response to item F5 'How many times is 0.1 greater than 0.01?' were to give the powers of 10 on either side of the correct answer which was 10. 10 per cent of the pupils gave the answer 100 and 8 per cent gave 1; it is possible but unlikely that some of these errors could be due to a miscounting of the decimal places. In any case, the fact that a power of ten was given is an indication that some understanding of the concept was present in the 18 per cent of pupils who made these errors.

5.19 Finally, in relation to the decimals cluster, it is worth noting that the rates of omitting items F4 and F5 were higher than those of F1, F2 and F3 in the cluster by about 10 per cent, possibly due to unfamiliarity with the type of questions or to some aspect of their language.

Adding and subtracting fractions

5.20 In *Primary survey report No. 1* the item cluster from the sub-category computation (fractions) concerned the addition of fractions. Some error analysis was available for the cluster and it indicated that the proportion of pupils who used the strategy of adding numerators and denominators (eg $\frac{1}{4} + \frac{1}{2} = \frac{2}{6}$) increased as the fractions became more complex. Further coding of errors carried out on items in the proportions of correct responses and rates of omission enables a more detailed analysis to be made of pupils' strategies.

5.21 Items which appeared to induce pupils to add numerators and denominators can be placed in three broad categories according to the proportions of pupils who used the strategy:

(i)   Denominators the same

Item	Correct	Omitting item	Adding numerators and denominators
	%	%	%
$\frac{3}{10} + 1\frac{7}{10} + \frac{8}{10}$	39	15	4
$1\frac{1}{4} + 1\frac{3}{4}$	62	8	6
$\frac{6}{10} + \frac{3}{10}$	72	2	8
$\frac{2}{5} + \frac{3}{5}$	60	7	13

(ii)   Different denominators: All halves, quarters or eighths.

Item	Correct	Omitting item	Adding numerators and denominators
	%	%	%
$1\frac{1}{2} + 2\frac{5}{8} + 1\frac{1}{4}$	25	27	10
$2\frac{1}{4} + 1\frac{1}{8}$	35	15	12
$\frac{1}{4} + \frac{1}{2}$	58	5	13

(iii)   Different denominators: At least one other than halves, quarters, eighths.

Item	Correct	Omitting item	Adding numerators and denominators
	%	%	%
$\frac{2}{3} + \frac{1}{4} + \frac{1}{12}$	30	21	14
$\frac{1}{6} + \frac{2}{3}$	37	7	21
$\frac{4}{5} + \frac{3}{10}$	33	16	21
$\frac{1}{2} + \frac{1}{3}$	33	9	24

5.22 Within these categories items requiring the addition of three fractions appear to induce the strategy less often than when two fractions are added, but this may be because they are omitted more frequently by those pupils who would otherwise use it.

5.23 The survey included fewer subtraction items but responses to several of them indicated the use of a parallel strategy; subtracting numerators and denominators. This strategy was not used when the denominators were the same.

Item	Correct	Omitting item	Subtracting numerators and denominators
	%	%	%
$2\frac{3}{16} - 1\frac{3}{4}$	16	29	3
$\frac{3}{4} - \frac{1}{2}$	48	18	12
$\frac{9}{12} - \frac{1}{6}$	34	13	17
$\frac{8}{9} - \frac{1}{3}$	31	19	17

5.24 The general level of the use of the strategy of subtracting numerators and denominators is similar to that of the parallel strategy in the case of addition items. It is very much lower in the item $2\frac{3}{16} - 1\frac{3}{4}$ where the strategy produces the result $1\frac{0}{12}$; possibly a number of pupils who would normally use the strategy recognised the anomaly and either substituted a different one or omitted the item.

5.25 A variation on the addition/subtraction of numerators and denominators may be employed by a small but consistent proportion of pupils. This consists of adding or subtracting the numerators (according to the operation indicated) and then placing the result over the largest denominator. It is worth noting that this strategy gives the correct answer if the denominators of the fractions are the same ($\frac{1}{5} + \frac{2}{5} = \frac{3}{5}$).

Item	Response	Giving response %
$1\frac{1}{2} + 2\frac{5}{8} + 1\frac{1}{4}$	$4\frac{7}{8}$	2
$\frac{2}{3} + \frac{1}{4} + \frac{1}{12}$	$\frac{4}{12}$	2
$\frac{4}{5} + \frac{3}{10}$	$\frac{7}{10}$	3
$\frac{8}{9} - \frac{1}{3}$	$\frac{7}{9}$	3
$\frac{3}{4} - \frac{1}{2}$	$\frac{2}{4}$ (or $\frac{1}{2}$)	3
$\frac{9}{12} - \frac{1}{6}$	$\frac{8}{12}$	4
$\frac{1}{2} + \frac{1}{4}$	$\frac{2}{4}$ (or $\frac{1}{2}$)	4
$\frac{3}{10} + 1\frac{7}{10} + \frac{8}{10}$	$1\frac{18}{10}$	6
$\frac{1}{6} + \frac{2}{3}$	$\frac{3}{6}$	6

5.26 The evidence provided by the results of the fraction items considered here suggests that inappropriate strategies are adopted more frequently when the denominators of the fractions are different and less familiar to the pupils. The two factors are probably independent to some extent for 1 in 8 pupils gave the response $\frac{2}{6}$ to the item $\frac{1}{4} + \frac{1}{2}$ where the denominators are different but the fractions are familiar to nearly all pupils.

Generalised arithmetic: equations

5.27 In items concerned with equations, letters (or other symbols) stand for numbers, for sets of numbers, or, generally, operate as variables. A high proportion of pupils could determine the value of a symbol in equations such as those shown below and few pupils failed to attempt them. The different sizes of the numbers involved were probably responsible for the difference of about 15 per cent in the number of pupils answering items M1 and M2 correctly.

5.28 When the relation between the numbers in an equation was expressed verbally instead of using an abstract symbol, the proportion correct rose to about 90 per cent and only 2 per cent omitted M3.

5.29 On the other hand, when the relationship and task were expressed more abstractly as in the multiple choice item M4, there was a marked fall in the number of correct responses. Nevertheless nearly 30 per cent chose the correct response and a further 14 per cent decided that subtraction was involved by putting a ring round $y - 10$ rather than $10 + y$ or $10y$. Nearly a quarter selected the alternative in which the letter and number were added, possibly cued by the word 'added' in the instructions.

5.30 M5 is another item concerned with numbers in a similar relationship to those already discussed. Here, the sum of two numbers was given in a symbolic form as $M + N = 4$, so each letter could take several values not just one. Some different values for N were given and the corresponding values of M were to be provided in tabular form.

Item		Correct	Omitting item
		%	%
M1	$51 + \blacktriangle = 90$	72	5
M2	$12 - \blacksquare = 8$	86	5

		% correct	% Omitting item
M3	Two numbers added together make 20. If one number is 8 what is the other?	90	2

			choosing each alternative	Omitting item
M4	Two numbers added together make 10. If one number is y, which of these will the other be?		%	%
		$10 - y$	29	10
		$10 + y$	23	
	Put a ring round the	$y - 10$	14	
	correct one.	$10y$	17	

M5   Fill in the values of M in this table according to the equation $M + N = 4$.

N	0	1	2	3	4	5
M	4					

						Given by	Omitted by
Correct responses	3	2	1	0		24%	32%
					-1	17%	36%
Other responses	5	6	7	8	9	19%	

5.31 About a quarter of the pupils gave the correct values of M corresponding to $N = 1, 2, 3$ and 4, which were positive integers or zero, but the negative value of M corresponding to $N = 5$ was, not surprisingly, a little more difficult. About one fifth of the pupils appear to have added 4 to each value of N.

5.32 The results of M5 raise questions about the extent of pupils' difficulties with the tabular presentation and with the idea that symbols can take various values and not just one. Item M6 has both these features but 52 per cent of the pupils gave the correct answer. The task, however is to substitute values of a variable on one side of an equation in order to evaluate a variable on the other side, and this is easier than dealing with two variables on the same side. This is demonstrated both by the higher facility of M6 compared with M5 and also by the lower rate of omitting the item (14 per cent).

M6　Fill in the values of n in this table according to the equation $n = m + 1$

m	1	2	3	4	5
n	2				

					Given by	Omitted by
Correct response		3	4	5	6	52%	14%
Other response		4	6	8	10	23%	

5.33 Nearly one quarter of the pupils apparently doubled the value of m to obtain the corresponding values of n. If this result is looked at in relation to the coded incorrect response to M5, it can be seen that a similar strategy has been followed by 20 to 25 per cent of pupils in response to both items viz: note the relation between the values of the variables which are given in the questions and fill in the table by repeating the same relation.

M5

N	0	
M	4	

Relation noted:

$M = N + 4$

M6

m	1	
n	2	

$n = 2m$

5.34 What is not clear from this analysis is whether pupils who followed this strategy did not understand the symbolic relationships $M + N = 4$ and $n = m + 1$ or simply ignored them. Another question also arises in relation to the use of the strategy in M6 where the relation between the values of m and n in the table could be seen either as $n = 2m$ or $n = m + 1$: it is possible that some of the 52 per cent of pupils who got the correct answer did so by using the numbers given in the table rather than the relationship between the letters.

5.35 A different sort of item in the equations cluster demonstrates the use of symbols as 'place holders'. In these items the symbols in the equations are effectively ignored as Kuchermann* has pointed out in relation to similar items used by the Concepts in School Mathematics & Science (CSMS) project at Chelsea College.

* D Kuchemann (1978). *Children's understanding of numerical variables.* Mathematics in schools 7, 4 23-26.

5.36 The CSMS items were (proportions correct are for third year secondary school pupils):

	Correct response	Given by
$a + b = 43, a + b + 2 = \underline{\hspace{1cm}}$	45	97%
$n - 246 = 762, n - 247 = \underline{\hspace{1cm}}$	761	74%

M7
        n stands for a number
         $n + 4 = 21$
        so $n + 5 =$ _____

	Given by
Correct response 22	*66%*
Other response 20	*1%*
Omitted	*6%*

M8
        B stands for a number
         $B - 9 = 21$
        so $B - 10 =$ _____

	Given by
Correct response 20	*51%*
Other response 22	*11%*
Omitted	*8%*

5.37 The basic structure of the CSMS items is the same as the APU pair, although the presentation is different and the numbers used are larger, especially in the 'subtraction' item. The level of performance is, not surprisingly, higher for the secondary pupils but the relative difficulty of the two types of item remains the same. Furthermore the proportion of CSMS secondary pupils who responded to the 'subtraction' item by adding instead of subtracting one from the answer to the previous equation (n-247 = 763) was 13 per cent about the same as the proportion of primary pupils in the APU item M8 (11 per cent) who used the same strategy.

5.38 A verbal equivalent of M7 and M8 produced a higher success rate in the APU survey and was omitted by fewer pupils.

M9

	Correct	*Omitting item*
	%	*%*
In thirteen years time I will be 32		
How old will I be in fourteen years time?	*78*	*2*

5.39 This comparison of M9 with M7 and M8 gives some idea of the extent of pupils' difficulty in handling symbols at this age.

5.40 In summary, the items discussed in this section indicate that pupils' ease of interpretation of relationships between variables depends on the number of symbols used to express the relationships (two letter symbols, one letter, verbal) the type of task (solving equations, evaluating expressions) and the form of the relationship between the symbols (a symbol on either side of the equation, two symbols on one side).

Reading graphs and scales

5.41 Graphs and scales are used in many areas of mathematics and so the items discussed in these sections come from several sub-categories of the assessment framework. The items are referred to by their sub-category code letters which are given in Chapter 4 (see 000) as follows:

R   Money, time, mass, temperature

E   Number concepts (whole numbers)

L   Probability and data representation

Scales

5.42 The items Ra,b,c,d contain diagrams of a thermometer scale extending through zero into negative temperatures. In each case the scale is graduated at 2° intervals and numbered at 10° intervals. In Ra, 85 per cent of the pupils gave the correct reading at a marked and numbered point on the scale (10°C). At a marked but unnumbered point in Rb the proportion correct fell to 34 per cent. The correct reading is 4°; 18 per cent gave the answer as 2°C and 7 per cent responded with 7°C. Both these incorrect answers could be obtained by counting each graduated interval as 1° but starting the count at different points on the scale — from 0°C to obtain the response 2°C and from the lowest mark on the scale to obtain 7°C. Alternatively, some pupils may have arrived at 7°C by counting down 3° from the 10° mark.

5.43 The temperature indicated in item Rc was correctly read by 28 per cent of the pupils. This temperature (15°C) is at a point on the scale which is neither numbered nor marked. The answer 12½°C could be obtained by counting each graduated interval as 1°, starting from the 10° graduation. 17 per cent of the pupils gave this answer, a similar proportion to the response which could have been obtained by the same method in Rb. A further 10 per cent thought the answer was 12°C; these pupils may have counted only the whole number of graduated intervals after 10°C.

5.44 The below zero reading in the fourth item in this group, Rd, was given correctly by 21 per cent. 37 per cent of the wrong answers were various combinations of the following three errors:

(i)   counting the graduated intervals as 1° instead of 2°;

(ii)   using the lowest mark on the scale as zero;

(iii) giving a positive instead of a negative reading.

5.45 The most common incorrect answer given was 11°, a combination of errors (ii) and (iii). 18 per cent gave this result while a further 7 per cent gave the answer as 1°C which is a compound of all three errors.

5.46 The rates of omission were about the same for all four items in this group although marginally lower for Ra. Thus, pupils were not particularly put off by being asked to read a below zero temperature in Rd. However, as 23 per cent gave a positive number in answer to this item it is possible that they either did not notice or were unaware of the significance of the temperature reading relative to zero.

R

What is the reading on each of these thermometers:

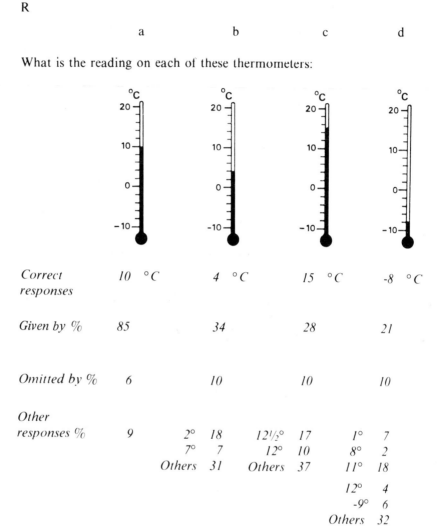

	a	b	c	d
Correct responses	10 °C	4 °C	15 °C	-8 °C
Given by %	85	34	28	21
Omitted by %	6	10	10	10
Other responses %	9	2° 18 7° 7 Others 31	12½° 17 12° 10 Others 37	1° 7 8° 2 11° 18 12° 4 -9° 6 Others 32

5.47 Some items in the number concepts (whole numbers) sub-category required pupils to place numbers on a graduated but incompletely numbered number line. Pupils' performance on these items can usefully be compared with their responses to the R group of items. In Ela 70 per cent of pupils correctly placed the number 4 on the line, compared with 57 per cent who indicated the correct position of the zero in Elb. In the latter case 11 per cent placed the zero to the left of -1 and a further 16 per cent located it at the mark on the line furthest to the left. Thus 1 in 6 pupils supposed that zero must be located at the end of the scale; in Rd 7 per cent gave a response suggesting that a similar assumption was made even though the zero point was marked on the scale.

E1

Put the numbers 4 and 0 in their correct places on this number line.

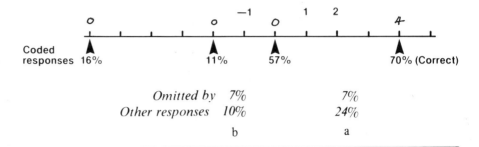

Omitted by	7%	7%
Other responses	10%	24%
	b	a

5.48 The characteristics of the number line items are different in several respects from those concerning the temperature scale: the scale is horizontal instead of vertical, each marked interval represents one unit not two and the context relates simply to numbers. Further, the task is the converse of that of the R items, for scale numbers are given in the questions and are not provided by the pupils. Any of these features, or a combination of them, could result in the difference in performance between the easiest items Ra and E1a (85 and 70 per cent respectively). However, the proportion giving correct responses to E2a and b was over 80 per cent, about the same as in the case of Ra, and it seems likely therefore that some pupils in E1a were confused by the absence of a zero and/or the presence of a negative number. The rates of omission of the E items were marginally lower than those of the R items.

E2

Put the numbers 3 and 5 in their correct places on this number line.

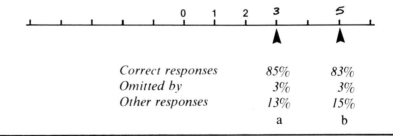

Correct responses	85%	83%
Omitted by	3%	3%
Other responses	13%	15%
	a	b

Graphs

5.49 The graphical items L1, L2 and L3 each include two scales and reading the graphs involves both types of task set in the E and R items. That is, a number is given which has to be located on one of the scales (as in the E items) and then another number is to be read on the second scale (as in the R items) which corresponds to the first. The correspondence is represented by the form and presentation of the graph.

L1

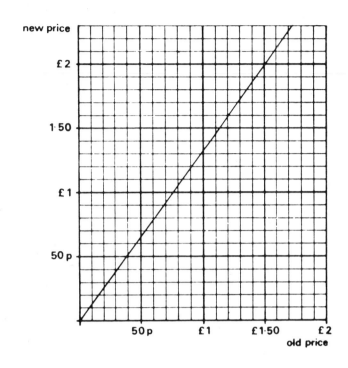

This graph shows new prices compared with old prices.

Facilities

a. What is the new price of something with
an old price of £1.50?   *£2* _ _ _ _ _ _ *51%*

b. What was the old price of something with
a new price of £1.20?   *90p or £0.90 26%*

                                                      75p or £0.75
c. What is the old price of something   *76p or £0.76 19%*
   with a new price of £1?   *77p or £0.77*

Correct responses are given above, other responses below:

	%			%			%
a *£1.10 to £1.20*	*3*	*b.* *£1.60*	*5*	*c.* *70p to 80p*	*9*
50p	*4*	*50p*	*3*	*£1.30 to £1.40*	*5*
Other responses	*28*	*Other responses*	*44*	*50p*	*18*
Omitted by	*15*	*Omitted by*	*22*	*£1.50*	*7*
				Other responses	*25*
				Omitted by	*19*

5.50 These situations provide possibilities for the sort of errors already listed in relation to the E and R items and additional ones such as starting with the wrong scale and misunderstanding the nature of the graph.

L2

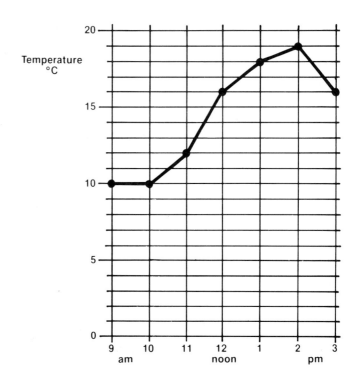

This was the temperature in a class room on one summer day.

			Correct response given by
a.	What was the temperature at 11 a.m.?	_12_	77%
b.	When was it warmest?	_2 pm_	81%

Other responses

a.	10°	5%	b.	12 noon	2%
	10½	<1%		19°	5%
	Others	14%		Others	8%
	Omitted by	4%		Omitted by	5%

5.51 Items L.1a, b and c follow a similar pattern to Ra, b and c. In L1a both scale points involved in the reading are marked and numbered, while in L1b they are marked but not numbered. L1c requires pupils to read an unmarked and unnumbered point on the horizontal scale although the vertical scale point is both graduated and numbered. The success rates for these items also follow a similar pattern of fall to those of Ra, b and c but at a somewhat lower level, especially L1a:

	a %	b %	c %
R	85	34	28
L1	51	26	19

5.52 The considerable difference in the proportion of correct responses between Ra and L1a could be due to the apparent greater complexity of the latter item. However, L2a is an item with the same task structure as L1a and 77 per cent of the pupils gave the correct answer. The differences between L1a and L2a are that both scales in L2a are graduated at unit intervals. They represent distinctive measures (time and temperature) whereas prices are the quantities on both the scales of L1, and the form of the graph is less regular. Perhaps most decisively, pupils are more familiar with graphs representing changes in temperature with time than with conversion graphs. The omission rates probably give some indication of pupils' familiarity in these cases: the R items were omitted by 10 per cent or fewer pupils, the L items by between 16 and 23 per cent but L2 by only 4 per cent. Responses which suggested that a few pupils had read the graph the wrong way round were given to each L1 item:

L1 items:	a	b	c
Response	£1.10 to £1.20	£1.60	£1.30 to £1.40
Given by	3%	5%	5%

5.53 As the scales in L2a represent different quantities it would appear to be less likely that this error would be made. In fact barely 1 per cent of the pupils gave the response 10½ which suggests that they began at the wrong scale.

5.54 The item L2b requires the pupils to read the time scale at a particular point on the graph (that representing the warmest temperature. 81 per cent gave the correct response. 5 per cent gave the warmest temperature (19°C) rather than the time it occurred; these pupils had probably misread the question rather than read the graph the wrong way.

5.55 One type of error made in the response to the R items was miscounting or miscalculating the graduated intervals on the thermometer scale. This error did not occur in the L1 items where each graduated interval represented 10 units, but it did appear in L3 where the intervals on the vertical scale represented 20 feet. 35 per cent gave answers in the interval 45 to 55 feet which were counted as correct, and a further 5 per cent wrote responses which were within 5 feet of the ends of that interval and were considered to be incorrect. Some 13 per cent gave answers between 20 and 30 feet which suggests that these pupils had counted each

L3

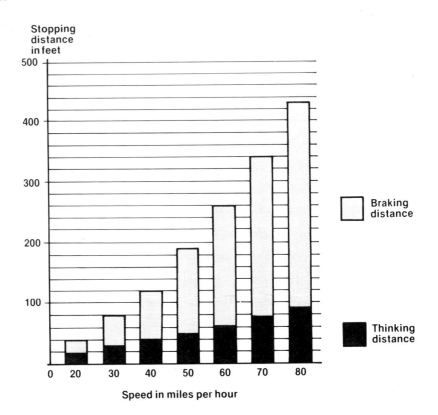

a. What is the thinking distance for a driver   *Correct response*
    travelling at 50 m.p.h?   *given by*

                                       50 feet   *35%*
                                       ─ ─ ─ ─

b. What is the braking distance for a driver
    travelling at 30 m.p.h?   50 feet   *20%*
                                       ─ ─ ─ ─

c. What is the stopping distance for a driver
    travelling at 80 m.p.h?

                                      430 feet   *18%*
                                       ─ ─ ─ ─

Other responses:

a.		b.		c.	
40–45 ft	*5%*	*40–45 ft*	*5%*	*420–425 ft*	*4%*
55–60 ft		*55–60 ft*		*435–440 ft*	
20–30 ft	*13%*	*20–30 ft*	*13%*	*410–420 ft*	*10%*
180–200 ft	*9%*	*80 ft*	*14%*	*Others*	*54%*
Others	*27%*	*Others*	*38%*	*Omitted by*	*15%*
Omitted by	*11%*	*Omitted by*	*11%*		

graduated interval as 10 feet. The same proportion also gave answers between 20 and 30 feet to L3b presumably for the same reason, and in response to L3c 10 per cent appeared to commit the same error in writing answers between 410 or 420 feet. These proportions are a good deal lower than the proportion of pupils making similar types of error in response to the R items — in which case the proportion is around 25 per cent. The difference does not appear to be due to the frequent occurrence of a different type of error in L3. The only other error to occur relatively frequently in L3a (9 per cent) and L3b (13 per cent) was giving the answer for stopping distance instead of thinking distance and braking distance respectively and the pupils who did this appear to have counted the intervals correctly.

5.56 Finally in this section, there were one or two errors probably due to a misunderstanding of the nature of the graphs involved. In L1, for example, 4 per cent gave 50p as their answer to L1a and 3 per cent gave the same response to L1b. A much higher number (18 per cent) also wrote 50p as their answer to L1c while another 7 per cent gave £1.50. In L3 about 5 per cent thought that 10° was the temperature at 11 am and this could be simply a misreading.

5.57 Summarising the results of items in this cluster, the success rate for reading scales was found to be high as long as the reading was at a graduated point on the scale and the point was numbered. If these conditions did not obtain there was a steep decline in performance. A similar pattern held for reading graphs except that performance tended to be lower than for reading scales, especially when the context was unfamiliar. A relatively high proportion of errors appeared when scales were graduated at intervals other than one or ten units and some pupils also had problems with the position of zero on a scale.

Conclusions

5.58 In this chapter some mathematical topics have been selected for more detailed analysis than it was possible to undertake for *Primary survey report No. 1*. Analysis of the various responses to items of related content within a cluster revealed the particular features of the items which presented difficulties for pupils and gave some indication of the strategies they used to tackle them.

6 The survey results

The aims of the mathematics surveys

6.1 The main aims of the mathematics surveys are to obtain an overall picture of performance and to monitor changes in that picture. These aims are different from those of the more familiar kinds of assessment procedure such as examinations. The purpose of the latter is to focus on the individuals taking the tests by placing them in order of merit or by deciding whether they have attained specified criteria of competency such as a pass mark or stated objectives of learning.

6.2 In the monitoring surveys, although individuals are tested, their performances are merged into the total picture which is the object of the assessment. It is not necessary for all those contributing to the total to take the same test, nor is there any need for all pupils in the target age group to be tested, since statistical procedures are available which enable the overall picture to be validly predicted from a relatively small sample.

6.3 Full details of the sampling procedure were given in *Primary survey report No. 1.* Its purpose is to produce a national representative sample of 11 year olds. It is not designed to make comparisons between individual pupils, schools and authorities, and consequently such comparisons cannot be made validly with the data obtained. This is also true of the sub-samples of pupils who took either the attitude or practical mathematics assessments. Individual pupils did the tests anonymously and took only some of the assessment materials. The overall sample was satisfactorily representative; 90 per cent of the schools invited to participate did so.

Results and comparisons: a summary

Practical tests

6.4 The practical test results reported in Chapter 2 include those of some of the topics used in 1979. Where the topics were also part of the 1978 survey the results from the two years are compared. Results of topics used only in 1978 and not published in *Primary survey report No. 1* are also included in the chapter.

6.5 Few of the differences in responses to items included in both years were statistically significant. This applies only to the initial responses pupils made to the questions put to them; tester intervention following these inital responses tended to be more searching this year due to some differences in the briefing instructions in 1979 and this resulted in higher aided success rates.

6.6 The practical tests, some of which are described in this report, involved pupils in a wide range of tasks which included the assessment of skills (measuring, estimating, visualising and giving change) and the understanding of concepts (for example, probability, geometrical shape and fractions). Also examined were the strategies used in practical problems such as making a label for a tin and making a lump of plasticine weighing half of a given mass.

6.7 Most of the tasks involving measures and visualisation were successfully completed by a high proportion (often around 90 per cent) of pupils. The measurement of angles with a protractor was an exception; a 60° angle, for example, was measured accurately by about 45 per cent of the pupils.

6.8 When pupils' initial responses were followed up by the testers, some interesting features of their ideas about mathematical concepts were revealed. For example, in the probability topic many pupils gave predictions about the outcomes of tossing coins and throwing dice which were correctly based on the number of alternative outcomes, but they reverted to past experience or other devices to justify the results they obtained empirically. The geometric shape topic demonstrated that some pupils' classification of shape as rectangles depended upon extraneous perceptual features such as the orientation of the shape and the relative lengths of adjacent sides.

6.9 The practical problems evoked a variety of strategies. The task of making a label for a tin was a good example. In order to measure out the required length of the tin some pupils used string and a ruler, some used string only and others used a combination of tape and ruler. Others rolled the tin along the paper and marked points at the beginning and end of the circumference.

6.10 Several practical tasks required pupils to communicate their ideas and results, and a variety of methods involving words, graphs and symbols were recorded by the testers.

Attitude questionnaire

6.11 The attitude questionnaire assessed pupils' thoughts and feelings towards mathematics in general and to some individual mathematical topics. Scores on scales of liking, difficulty and utility were derived from the responses to statements about mathematics as a whole.

6.12 The liking scale score which could range from 0 to 34 had a mean of 21.6 in 1979 compared with 20.0 in 1978. The increase, which was significant statistically, was mainly accounted for by a tendency for pupils to shift from response categories reflecting a dislike of mathematics to an undecided position. The difficulty scale has a range of 0 to 22, the higher scores indicating that mathematics is perceived to be easy. The mean score on this scale was 11.8 in 1979 and that on the utility scale (range 0 to 24) was 20.4. Neither the difficulty nor the utility scale scores changed significantly in comparison with 1978.

6.13 There were few statistically significant changes in pupils' perceived liking of and difficulty with the mathematical topics listed in other parts of the questionnaire. There were few differences in the responses of boys and girls in relation to their liking of mathematics in general and how useful they thought it to be. Certain statements on the difficulty scale which reflected confidence in mathematical ability were significantly more likely to be agreed to by boys than by girls. Several mathematical topics in the geometry and measures categories were liked and found easier by more boys than girls.

Written tests: Sub-category and item results

6.14 The basic data from the written tests were the facilities (success rates) for the 647 items and the proportions of pupils omitting each of them. For many of the items detailed analyses were made of the various responses pupils gave to them.

6.15 The 647 test items were grouped into 13 sub-categories of mathematics and the mean scores of these groupings were computed. In *Primary survey report No. 1* percentage mean scores were obtained for each sub-category by a procedure which involved averaging the success rates of items in the sub-category. This time a method of scaling item difficulty and pupils' scores was used.

6.16 As Northern Ireland pupils participated for the first time comparisons between the 1978 and 1979 survey results were based on the test scores of pupils from England and Wales only. The comparisons were made on scaled scores from the two surveys and showed that the difference in mean scores between the two years is significant statistically only in the two computation sub-categories. In these two sub-categories there was a rise which represents an improvement of between one and two more questions answered correctly in a 50 item test. Although the probability of a statistically significant difference arising by chance is small in this case (less than 1 in 20), the possibility nevertheless exists, and so confirmation or otherwise of the reality of the change in the scores in these sub-categories or any trend in the scores must await the results of future surveys.

6.17 The differences in the two computation sub-categories in both cases applied generally across the items and not to any particular area of content. As the sample size for items is less than that for sub-categories, because of the way the tests are designed, it is less likely that difference in item facilities between the two surveys will be statistically significant. Consequently the general picture in 1979 so far as individual items are concerned is much as it was described in *Primary survey report No. 1*. However, further details in that picture have been filled in this year for some clusters of items: line symmetry, concept of decimals, adding and subtracting fractions, equations, and reading graphs and scales. The account of results in these areas show more clearly than in 1978 how responses to particular items can be interpreted by contrasting them with responses to other items of related content.

6.18 For example, it was noted in *Primary survey report No. 1* that about 80 per cent of pupils could draw the correct image of a simple shape in a vertically positioned mirror while only about 15 per cent could do so if the mirror was placed obliquely. However, the error analysis for the latter item in 1979 showed that over 40 per cent of the incorrect drawings included some reversal of the object and were not random responses. Few pupils omitted either the vertical or the oblique mirror items so the latter were not seen as unfamiliar in spite of the low rate of success. But nearly a quarter of the pupils omitted items in which the term 'line of symmetry' was used although, where only one line was involved, the success rates were much higher than those for items concerned with drawing images in oblique mirrors. The analyses of the other item clusters were based on similar types of evidence.

Written tests: background variables

6.19 As in the case of individual items there was little difference between the 1978 and 1979 survey results within the different groupings of the background variables. That is, pupils from schools in non-metropolitan authorities had higher scores than those from schools in metropolitan authorities. Lower scores were associated with higher proportions of pupils taking free school meals. Schools with higher pupil teacher ratios tended to obtain higher mean scores, and those with fewer pupils in the 10-plus age group also tended to get higher scores. Boys had higher mean scores than girls in ten of the sub-categories but only five of these differences were statistically significant.

Caveats

6.20 *Primary survey report No. 1* gave caveats about interpreting results and relations in causal terms. Attribution for the levels of pupils' performance and the errors and explanations they make cannot be apportioned among the many possible contributing factors using the evidence obtained from the surveys. Neither can relations between performance and background variables be regarded as being necessarily due to direct or indirect causality.

6.21 In this report it is necessary to enter a further caveat about the comparisons made between the results of the 1978 and 1979 surveys. Survey data is subject to random fluctuations and it is important to distinguish these from differences due to real changes in scores. It is possible for random fluctuations alone to produce differences which are large enough to be statistically significant. At the level of statistical significance used (5 per cent) the probability of this happening is 1 in 20 or less. However, a large number of comparisons have been made and up to 1 in 20 of these could therefore be significant by chance. Thus no valid conclusions about trends in performance can be made from the results of the two surveys so far reported.

Developments in the monitoring programme

6.22 Development is continuing in the existing assessment procedures and new assessment materials are being piloted. The major area of current item development is concerned with problems, applications and investigations. Trials of written test items in this area are taking place and it is expected that the 1981 surveys will contain a number of them.

6.23 Related to these developments are changes being made to the assessment framework. One amendment, the inclusion of categories of context has been reported in Chapter 1. The other changes include further detailing of the outcomes category and completing the blank areas of the framework (see Figure 1.1) to accommodate problems, applications and investigations.

6.24 These amendments and additions to the assessment framework will be fully described in a subsequent report. They will enable the picture of mathematics performance to be structured and described more completely.

Appendix 1. The survey sample and data collection

1.1 The sampling strategy adopted for the second survey of 11 year old pupils' performance in mathematics was very similar to that used for the first. Full details are given in the report of that survey. In deciding the sampling strategy a balance has been struck between the need for a sample large enough to allow useful inferences concerning the national population to be drawn and the need to avoid overburdening either schools or individual pupils.

1.2 A two-stage sampling procedure was used in which a stratified sample of schools was drawn first and a sample of pupils chosen from each selected school by reference to their dates of birth. The proportion of pupils selected from each sample school varied according to the size of the 10-plus age group in the school (the larger the age group, the smaller the proportion of pupils sampled) since with this approach it is easier to predict the number of pupils who will be sampled at the second stage and more large schools are used making it more likely that a representative sample of these schools will be obtained.

1.3 Since only a sample of the pupils in each school is tested, the two-stage sampling procedure demonstrates the Assessment of Performance Unit's declared intention of monitoring performance nationally and not concerning itself with the performance of individual pupils or schools.

Impact on schools and pupils

1.4 Schools had the option of not participating and of withdrawing individual pupils from the testing if it was thought likely to cause them undue distress. Although large scale withdrawals would have had serious consequences for both the representativeness and size of the achieved sample it was felt that schools should be allowed this discretion. The extent to which it was exercised in this survey can be seen in Table A1.1. The effect of participation in the survey upon individual pupils was minimised by giving only a small number of the available items to each pupil and by keeping the testing sessions fairly short.

The survey sample

1.5 The target population was defined as all pupils born between 1 September 1967 and 31 August 1968, ie pupils whose eleventh birthday fell between 1 September 1978 and 31 August 1979 inclusive. This effectively meant that testing was conducted within a single school year-group in England and Wales. In Northern Ireland, however, where children transfer between year-groups on a different basis (dates of birth from 2 July to the following 1 July) and where most children follow a primary school course which finishes at age eleven, approximately five-sixths of the children tested were in the final year of primary schooling and one sixth were in their penultimate primary year. Pupils in special schools or special units within schools were excluded.

1.6 It was intended to test approximately 10,000 pupils in England, and about 2,500 in both Wales and Northern Ireland, ie about 1½ per cent and 5 per cent of the age group respectively. As described above the proportion of pupils in the age group sampled in each school depended on the number of pupils in the 10-plus age group in the school, and the following proportions were used:

Size of 10-plus age group	Proportion of age group tested
4 — 15 pupils*	All
16 — 30 pupils	$\frac{1}{2}$
31 — 45 pupils	$\frac{1}{3}$
Over 45 pupils	$\frac{1}{4}$

* Schools with fewer than four pupils in the relevant age group were excluded for administrative reasons.

1.7 In order to ensure that all regions of the country and all types and sizes of school were represented, the population of schools in England and Wales was stratified in four ways: by type of school, size of the 10-plus age group, by region and by location as shown below:

Type of school:	Junior
	Junior/infant/first and middle
	Middle/secondary
	Independent
Sizes of 10-plus age group:	4 – 15 pupils
	16 – 30 pupils
	31 – 45 pupils
	Over 45 pupils
Region:	North
	South
	Midlands
	Wales
Location:	In metropolitan counties.
	In non-metropolitan counties.

1.8 Details of the local education authorities in each region and their designation as metropolitan or non-metropolitan are given in Table A1.2 (page 94).

1.9 The schools in Northern Ireland were stratified by size of age group (categorised in the same way as in England and Wales) and by management type:

Management type of school:
    Controlled — Managed by Boards
    Maintained — Managed by statutory committees
    Voluntary — Managed by individual managers

1.10 It is not appropriate to use school type as a stratification variable in Northern Ireland due to the fact that 94 per cent of the schools are defined as Primary schools. The other 6 per cent of schools are evenly split between Junior and Preparatory.

Written tests

1.11 A sample of 1,098 schools was randomly selected, within the stratification framework, and their headteachers contacted and asked if they, and their staffs, could take part in the survey. Table A1.1 gives details of the respone rate achieved which is acceptably high, 978 schools providing data for the analyses described in this report.

Table A1.1 *The sample of schools and pupils*

a)   The sample of schools

	Number of schools			
	England	Wales	N. Ireland	TOTAL
Invited to take part	732	192	174	1098
Unable to take part	28	5	7	40
Did not reply	11	7	14	32
Pupil data form not returned or received too late*	14	6	9	29
Tests not received at NFER	9	2	6	17
Tests returned unused	2	–	–	2
Tests received	668	172	138	978

	England	Wales	N. Ireland	TOTAL
Practical Schools taking part	166	19	19	204
Attitudes Schools taking part	153	39	17	209

b)   The sample of pupils

	Number of pupils			
	England	Wales	N. Ireland	TOTAL
Total sample	10669	2179	1865	14713
Absent	108	12	7	127
Withdrawn	49	10	5	64
Number completing tests	10512	2157	1853	14522

* See account opposite of procedure for preserving pupil anonymity.

1.12 The total sample of pupils for whom tests were sent to schools was 14,713 and after absences and withdrawals the tests from 14,522 pupils were returned to the NFER for marking (Table A1.1). Some of these were rejected subsequently for various reasons, eg faulty test booklets, answers illegible, etc. In the event, test scores form 14,180 pupils were included in the analyses described in this report.

Practical tests

1.13 A sub-sample was randomly selected for the practical testing from the schools and pupils taking the written tests. Twenty seven testers visited 204 schools and tested approximately 1,200 pupils.

Attitude survey

1.14 A different sub-sample of approximately 1,250 pupils in 209 schools was randomly selected for the investigation of pupils' attitudes to mathematics.

Anonymity

1.15 The APU is concerned about the anonymity of pupils taking part in the survey and it is agreed that pupils' names should not appear on any of the materials used in their assessments or be known outside the school. The procedure which has been adopted ensures the anonymity of the pupils tested while allowing checks to be made on the data.

1.16 A two-stage system is used in which teachers are asked to enter on specially designed pupil data forms the date of birth and sex of each of the pupils selected for the sample. These forms, made up of sets of direct-copying paper, are so designed that one copy is wider than the others to allow the name of the pupil to be entered alongside the date of birth. This copy is retained by the school. On receipt of the other copies of the form containing only the date of birth and sex of each pupil the NFER allocates a pupil reference number to each entry and one copy now containing the reference number as well as date of birth and sex is returned to the school so that the number can be entered on the school's copy containing the names of the pupils. Each test and questionnaire booklet subsequently sent to a school has one of the reference numbers allocated to the selected pupils in that school printed in advance on the front page. Names are not required and the test data are linked only to a reference number. The only link between the pupil's name and reference number is held by the school. Thus the pupil's anonymity is not only preserved but also seen to be preserved.

1.17 It has also been agreed that schools and local education authorities will not be identified in any document or report produced by NFER for transmission to the DES, the Welsh Office, the DENI or for general publication.

Data collection

1.18 The NFER followed its normal procedure of asking local education authorities for permission to contact schools under their control. This was given in all but two cases in which the authority felt there were particular factors which argued for exclusion of the schools. The schools were first contacted in late January/early February 1979, and were informed of the consultations which had already taken place with their LEAs and of the guaranteed anonymity of pupils, schools and LEAs. They were asked to agree to administer a test of about 50 minutes to some of the pupils in the age group.

1.19 Instructions for the testing were sent to schools about three weeks before the testing week and were followed immediately by the tests themselves. Teachers were asked to make sure that each pupil completed the booklet allocated by a reference number to him or her. The way in which pupil reference numbers were allocated to the test booklets ensured that the 26 different written tests (see Chapter 4) were distributed at random throughout the sample of pupils. Testing was carried out in the week beginning 7 May 1979 and a further fortnight from the day of testing was allowed to test any pupil absent on that day.

1.20 Other information requested from the schools included the date of testing for each pupil or an indication of a pupil's absence or withdrawal, data concerning absenteeism and the numbers of pupils taking free school meals.

Table A1.2 *Counties in regions of England and Wales*

NORTH	MIDLANDS	SOUTH	WALES
Merseyside*	West Midlands*	Greater London*	Clwyd
Greater Manchester*	Hereford & Worcester	Bedfordshire	Dyfed
South Yorkshire*	Salop	Berkshire	Gwent
West Yorkshire*	Staffordshire	Buckinghamshire	Gwynedd
Tyne & Wear*	Warwickshire	East Sussex	Mid Glamorgan
Cleveland	Derbyshire	Essex	Powys
Cumbria	Leicestershire	Hampshire	South Glamorgan
Durham	Lincolnshire	Hertfordshire	West Glamorgan
Humberside	Northamptonshire	Isle of Wight	
Lancashire	Nottinghamshire	Kent	
North Yorkshire	Cambridgeshire	Oxfordshire	
Northumberland	Norfolk	Surrey	
Cheshire	Suffolk	West Sussex	
		Isle of Scilly	
		Avon	
		Cornwall	
		Devon	
		Dorset	
		Gloucestershire	
		Somerset	
		Wiltshire	

* Metropolitan counties

Northern Ireland Education and Library Boards

Belfast
North Eastern
Southern
South Eastern
Western

Table A1.3 *The obtained sample*

		Size of age group								
		4 − 15		16 − 30		31 − 45		46+	
		Pupils	Schools	Pupils	Schools	Pupils	Schools	Pupils	Schools
NORTH										
Non-	Junior	0	0	10	1	25	2	579	26
Met	J & I	112	12	158	15	158	13	247	14
	Middle	0	0	0	0	0	0	162	7
	Independent	0	0	13	2	4	1	12	1
Met	Junior	0	0	12	1	117	10	843	42
	J & I	20	2	174	17	257	24	238	16
	Middle	0	0	0	0	0	0	351	13
	Independent	12	1	13	1	4	1	16	1
MIDLANDS										
Non-	Junior	0	0	0	0	12	1	629	31
Met	J & I	133	14	135	13	159	13	249	16
	Middle	0	0	0	0	12	1	338	15
	Independent	12	1	21	2	24	2	14	1
Met	Junior	0	0	0	0	8	1	285	14
	J & I	0	0	35	3	72	7	145	8
	Middle	0	0	0	0	0	0	36	2
	Independent	0	0	9	1	0	0	9	1
SOUTH										
Non-	Junior	0	0	0	0	21	2	1035	52
Met	J & I	128	13	345	31	333	26	507	34
	Middle	0	0	0	0	0	0	602	24
	Independent	11	2	114	9	28	2	70	4
Met	Junior	0	0	13	1	32	2	624	29
	J & I	0	0	109	9	174	14	206	15
	Middle	0	0	0	0	0	0	136	5
	Independent	14	1	47	4	10	1	30	2
WALES										
	Junior	0	0	26	3	110	10	810	51
	J & I	282	34	329	28	250	20	228	15
	Independent	8	1	30	3	0	0	0	0
NORTHERN IRELAND										
	Controlled	183	21	320	27	267	14	156	5
	Voluntary	0	0	0	0	0	0	39	3
	Maintained	276	30	190	17	217	13	212	8

Appendix 2. Statistical significance

The test of significance used for this report

1.1 The purpose of drawing a random sample is to allow statistical inferences to be made about the defined population from which it was taken. Different samples drawn from the same population are subject to variations in their characteristics, so that their mean scores differ both among themselves and from the mean of the population. The larger the sample, the more precise its mean will be as an estimate of the population mean.

1.2 If it is desired to compare the performance of pupils in different defined sub-populations (for example, pupils aged 10 years from Northern schools and pupils aged 10 years from Southern schools), then separate samples would be drawn from each sub-population. What is required is to decide whether any difference between the sample means reflects a real difference between the sub-population means and the classical statistical significance test is designed to do this. The procedure is to calculate the probability that a difference in the sample means of the observed magnitude or higher would be found if the sub-populations in fact had the same means. If the probability of getting the obtained difference is low (e.g. 5 per cent or 1 in 20 chances) on the assumption that the sub-populations are the same, then the difference between the sample means is said to be statistically significant at that level of probability (ie at the 5 per cent level). Such a significance test may also be viewed as a device for providing evidence about the direction of the difference, so that a statistically 'significant' result is strong evidence that the difference between the sub-population means is in the same direction as that of the sample means. A 'non-significant' result simply fails to provide such evidence.

1.3 Thus, if a difference between two sample means is significant at the 5 per cent level this only means that, if there was no difference between the sub-populations from which the samples were drawn, such a difference would be expected to arise by chance between no more than 1 pair of samples out of 20 (ie. 5 per cent). It follows that if 20 independent differences between sample means are tested at the 5 per cent level it is to be expected that one of them will be 'significant' *even if there is no real difference* between the sub-populations sampled. This proviso should be particularly noted in the contet of the data from the written tests and background variables where a very large number of significance tests have been carried out.

1.4 Statistical significance does not provide an indication of the educational significance of a difference between the defined populations. Thus, a statistically non-significant large difference between sample means may be more worthy of note for further investigation than a statistically significant small difference between sample means; the former needs to be supported statistically, but the latter might be of little interest educationally even if it was a real difference. Throughout this report therefore references are made to statistically significant results which must then be judged in relation to their possible educational significance and implications both of which are usually left to the reader.

The meaning of statistical significance

2.1 Throughout the analyses for this report statistical significance has been determined by computing the statistic $\overline{Z}$ described in Chapter 9 of *Fundamental statistics in psychology and education* by J P Guilford and B Fruchter, fifth edition, published in 1973 by McGraw-Hill. This statistic is computed by taking the ratio of the mean to the standard error of that mean, under the null-hypothesis that the mean is zero. The analyses for this report each compared two groups of pupils, a group being defined by a characteristic such as sex, size of age group, region of school etc. The mean difference and the standard error of this difference between the two groups enables a test statistic $\overline{Z}$ to be calculated. The null-hypothesis is that the mean difference between the two groups is zero. Tables of probability levels associated with the $\overline{Z}$ statistic allows this to be examined.

2.2 It is important to estimate the mean difference between the scores of groups and the standard error of this difference, as opposed to estimating the means and standard errors of the two groups and then calculating a t statistic, (also described in *Fundamental statistics in psychology and education*). The reason for this is that pupils from the same school perform more alike than those from the total population. Thus the standard error of the difference between two groups will, in general, be different from the pooled standard error of each group.

2.3 The standard error terms given by Guilford and Fruchter have been modified to make allowance for inflation (the 'design effect') arising from the use of a stratified cluster sample rather than a simple random sample. The design effect on the standard error of the sub-category scores is about 1.3 for the 1979 data and this has been used as an estimate of the design effect for the practical and attitude data as well for the data from the written tests.

2.4 Further details of the estimating procedures can be found in a technical supplement which is published separately from this report. (See paragraph A3/5.6, page 103).

Appendix 3. The work on the Rasch model

Relevance of the Rasch model to APU mathematics

1.1 One of the aims of the APU work in mathematics — and in the other lines of development also — is the long term monitoring of the performance of school pupils. Problems arise in studies of this type because as the curriculum changes, questions used in the assessment instruments may become increasingly irrelevant to the experience of the pupils tested. In addition new areas of mathematics may find their way into the curriculum and must be included in the survey assessments if the monitoring programme is to remain comprehensive.

1.2 Since normally the success rate expressed as the percentage of items answered correctly on a particular test depends upon the items included, it is not feasible simply to change items to keep pace with curriculum changes. There is no reason to suppose that the success rate obtained on one occasion is equivalent to one from another if between-times some of the items in the test have been replaced. To retain comparability of success rates despite changes in the test content it is necessary to be able to predict the effect upon pupils' scores of introducing new items which may be easier or more difficult than the old ones. If this can be done then the effect can be allowed for and the comparisons made between data obtained with different tests. The Rasch model offers a way of making allowance for the difficulty of the test items and hence offers a possible technical solution to the problem of monitoring performance on a changing curriculum.

1.3 Even if it is possible to render scores obtained with different tests comparable at a particular time, a problem remains when the same techniques are applied to compensate for curriculum change between testing occasions. If, for example, more geometry and less algebra were taught in schools in the future then the balance of the items used would be expected to change in favour of geometry. In this case, if it were necessary to amend the test material to accommodate the new curriculum, then doubts could be raised about the validity and meaning of a comparison of pupils performance when they have not studied the same curriculum. However meaning could still be given to a change in performance *within* geometry or a change *within* algebra although taken as a whole the 'mathematics' being assessed would be different. Of course the effects of curriculum changes (mirrored by changes in the assessment material) *within* a sub-category would still be felt and the 13 sub-categories adopted represent a compromise solution.

The Rasch model

2.1 The Rasch model is based on Georg Rasch's conception of 'objectivity'*. The idea is analogous to, for example, the measurement of length where any properly calibrated ruler may be used to measure a given distance. Similarly any set of items (a test) should give the same result when used to measure the performance of a given individual. Additionally, in the same way as different instruments for the measurement of length may be best in different circumstances (for example, a

---

* See A.S. Willmott & D. F. Fowles. *The Objective Interpretation of Test Performance* (1974). NFER

30cm ruler is inappropriate for measuring the length of a running track), so different tests will be more suitable for some individuals then others. However, Rasch argued that whichever test is used the measurements obtained should be on the same scale and thus comparable one with another.

2.2 What is required is to determine the position of each item in a test on a scale of difficulty (cf the scale markings on a ruler.) and for 'objectivity' these positions should be the same for all the people whose performance is to be measured. If a large number of items were calibrated in this way they could be used to construct a variety of tests all of which, because of the common system of item calibrations, would provide the same measurement for any given person. The idea that all the items in a test can be positioned on a single scale implies that their properties can be summarized in single values and that all of them are measuring a single facet of performance (sometimes called a 'unidimensional latent trait' of performance). Rasch suggested a model in which items are characterised only by their difficulty, and do indeed measure a unidimensional trait of performance. He proposed that the chance of any particular candidate getting a particular item right can be treated as depending on only these two qualities, the attainment of the person and the difficulty of the item.*.

2.3 The Rasch model is like any other model and cannot be expected to describe real data completely. Models are used because they are simplifications of reality that focus attention on aspects of interest and thus allow useful conclusions to be drawn. The adequacy with which the model describes the various patterns in the data is tested and this involves checking for example that the estimated item difficulties are indeed the same for candidates of any level of performance and that the measured performances do not depend on the particular items taken. Obviously there are many factors which effect the outcome when a particular person attempts a particular item which cannot be summarised in two

---

*One way of writing his model is:

$$P_{ij} = \frac{W^{(\beta_j - \delta_i)}}{1 + W^{(\beta_j - \delta_i)}}$$

where P_{ij} is the probability of a candidate with performance β_j getting an item with difficulty δ_i right and W is a constant.

This model has a number of statistical advantages outlined by Choppin but its prime advantage is its 'Objectivity' in Rasch's terms since the estimated difficulty of each item *relative to the others with which it is calibrated* will be the same for candidates of any performance level, and conversely each candidate's attainment will be measured to be the same by items of any difficulty.

It should be noted that the model is only concerned with *relative* difficulty and *relative* attainment. The scales do not have meaningful zero points, if one set of parameters ($\beta_1 \beta_2 \beta_3$ ...., $\delta_1 \delta_2 \delta_3$ ....) can be found to satisfy the equation above then clearly a further set ($\beta_1 + c, \beta_2 + c, \beta_3 + c,$ .... $\delta_1 + c, \delta_2 + c, \delta_3 + c$ ...... where c is any constant) will also satisfy it since, for example,

$$\beta_1 - \delta_2 = (\beta_1 + c) - (\delta_2 + c).$$

In the work described in this report the scales are anchored by giving an arbitrary value of 50 to the mean of the estimated item difficulties. The value of W is also arbitrary and has been set at 1.2457 since this gives a useful relationship between a pupil's scaled scores and the probability of getting an item of known difficulty right (see section A3.5).

Reference: B. Choppin *Item Banking and the Monitoring of Achievement*, (1978). NFER parameters but these additional factors are not essential to the measurement task as has been shown on a number of occasions.

Alternative strategies

3.1 It is appropriate at this point to mention some alternatives to the Rasch model which might be used instead to overcome the problem of changing assessment material.

3.2 Moderation procedures such as those used to check comparability in public examinations could be used. A panel of mathematics education experts might be asked to judge the relative difficulty of the new material against earlier material. Alternatively, or in addition, direct calibration of the new material against the old would be possible. The sample would take both the old tests and the new ones and the scores obtained from the new tests would be transformed so as to be comparable with those from the old.

3.3 It is easy to see that both these techniques could also be used to permit a variety of tests to be employed on any one occasion as well as to accommodate changing assessment materials. However, both raise problems of a serious nature. The accuracy of the moderation procedures would always be open to question and could only be empirically investigated by making use of some sort of statistical calibration procedure. The direct calibration of the tests would involve a considerable increase in the amount of testing time required from the pupils. However, most importantly, neither approach offers any advantages concerning the fundamental problem of monitoring performance on a changing curriculum which, as we have seen, concerns the meaning of comparisons between the performance of pupils with different curriculum backgrounds. An approach based on the Rasch model makes no more assumptions than these more traditional ones and offers a number of advantages. Not the least of these is that the user is alerted to the effects of the changing curriculum by movements in the way the data fits the model. For example, with a Rasch model approach routine checks of the stability of item difficulty parameters can reveal changes which reflect new emphases in the curriculum and thus provide data on the nature of these emphases.

The linked test design

4.1 The work on the APU mathematics surveys makes use of linked tests, that is tests with items in common, in order to calibrate all the items in each sub-category together.

Figure A3.1   *Two overlapping tests*

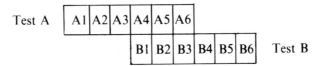

4.2 For example in Figure A3.1 two tests are shown in which questions A4, A5 and A6 are the same as B1 B2 B3 respectively. (Note that it is only for clarity that the items concerned are the last in one test and the first in the other; this would be unlikely in a practical design). Because of the items in common it is possible to exploit the Rasch model to place all the items in the two tests on a common scale. Firstly all the items in Test A are calibrated relative to one another (that is the relative difficulty of each is estimated from the response of the pupils who took Test A) and all the items in Test B are calibrated separately from the responses of the pupils who took Test B. To draw the two calibrations together, the difficulty estimates for all the items in one of the tests, say Test B, are adjusted until the items which are common to the two tests have the same mean estimated difficulty as in the other test, Test A. Once this is achieved all the items in both Tests A and B are positioned correctly relative to each other on a scale of difficulty. The adjustment is achieved by adding a constant factor to all the item difficulty estimates in the test being adjusted. This is an acceptable procedure because (as described in paragraphs 2. No. 2.1 — 2.3 above) it is only the relative difficulty of the items which is calibrated, the zero point is arbitrary.

4.3 In the primary mathematics surveys each sub-category is divided into six parts (see Chapter 4) in such a way that half of the items in each part are included in one adjacent part and the other half are included in the other as this diagram shows:

Figure A3.2 *The overlap between the six parts for each sub-category* (eg half of part 3 is contained in part 2 and half in part 4).

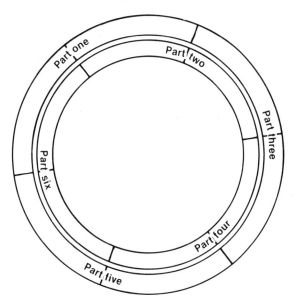

4.4 The common items are used as links by means of which the various parts are calibrated together. The procedure outlined above for two tests is repeatedly applied around the 'cartwheel', the items in part one being placed on the same scale as those in part two, part three, part four, part five, part six and so back to part one. It is of course rare for the parts to fit together perfectly, and any error is divided among the parts.

4.5 Once the linking process is completed scaled scores obtained from any of the parts are given equal weight as measurements of performance on the sub-category concerned. Thus, since an effective weighted sample of about 300 pupils answer the items in each sub-category part, about 1,800 weighted responses are available for the sub-category as a whole.

The performance scale used in the APU mathematics work

5.1 The scores reported in Chapter 4 are from a scale derived from the model which has been chosen because it gives a simple relationship between the probability of a pupil getting an item right and the difference between the scaled score of the pupil and the difficulty of the item (see Table A3.1).

Table A3.1 *Relationship of the difference between a pupil's scaled score and an item's difficulty and the probability of a correct response*

Pupils scaled score	Minus	Item's difficulty	Probability of getting item right
10			0.90
5			0.75
0			0.50
−5			0.25
−10			0.10

5.2 For example, if a large number of pupils whose scaled scores are 55 units attempt an item of difficulty 50 units about 75 per cent would be expected to get it right. On the other hand pupils with scaled scores of 40 units would have a probability of only .10 of getting an item of difficulty 50 units right.

5.3 As a further example the following item is taken from the sub-category on Symmetry, transformations and coordinates:

Draw in the line of symmetry on the shape.

5.4 This item has a Rasch difficulty of 47.7 units and the mean scaled score of the candidates from the 1979 sample in symmetry, transformations and coordinates is 51.2. The difference of 3.5 units gives a probability of the average pupil getting the item right of 0.68 which is not significantly different to the percentage of pupils who answered correctly (66 per cent). (The values will not necessarily be identical because with the test design used only one third of the pupils who contributed to the mean scaled sub-category score attempted any particular item and, the Rasch model is concerned with probabilities and cannot be expected to give a perfect prediction of real data.)

5.5 The relationship between the scaled scores reported in Chapter 4 and the more familiar way of expressing test scores as a percentage of correct responses is shown in Figure A3.3 for two tests of different difficulty. For example with the test of mean difficulty 50 units a score of 70 per cent gives a Rasch scaled score of about 54, whereas with the test of mean difficulty 55 units, 70 per cent converts to a scaled score of about 59. It can be seen from Figure A3.3 that to obtain any particular scaled score a pupil must answer a greater proportion of the items correctly on an easy test (lower mean difficulty) than on a harder one. Thus, allowance can be made for the inclusion of easier or harder items in a test and this has been done to mitigate the effects of the changes in the marking of some items in the 1979 tests (see paragraph 4.4). The mean performance scores reported in Chapter 4 for 1978 and 1979 can therefore be easily compared.

Figure A3.3 *The relationship between percentage test score and scaled score based on the Rasch model for tests of mean difficulty 50 and 55 units.*

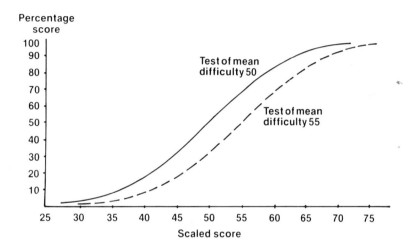

5.6 A number of tests have been carried out to determine the extent to which the Rasch model describes the data obtained. The results of these tests and other details concerning the technical procedures used in the survey are published separately in a technical supplement to this report which is obtainable on application to the Assessment of Performance Unit.

Appendix 4

Practical testers

Mr D Browne	St Christopher's R C Junior School, Liverpool
Mrs L Brown	Cambell Junior School, Dagenham
Mr R Bythell	Hunloke Park Primary School, Chesterfield
Mr M C Capper	Spalding County Primary School, Spalding
Mr S F Collier	Penryn County Junior School, Cornwall
Mrs L M Davy	Kings Copse County Primary School, Southampton
Mrs L Dungate	Lessness Heath Primary School, Belvedere
Mr R I Fairclough	St Pauls C E School, Chorley
Mr R E Freeman	Hollyhedge Primary School, West Bromwich
Mr C French	Walter de Merton Junior School, Watford
Miss S A Holcombe	Haringey Teachers' Centre, Tottenham
Mrs J Holloway	Fairlight Middle School, Brighton
Mr L Keen	Epping County Junior School, Epping
Mr D Maxwell	Teachers' Centre for Curriculum Development, North Shields
Mr R M McKinney	Avoniel P School, Belfast
Mr J Morris	North Hinksey C E Primary School, Oxford
Mr G M Peake	Burton Road J & I School, Barnsley
Mr B L H Rowe	St Columba's R C lst School, Bradford
Mr J Smith	St Joseph's P School, Co Antrim
Mr J H Thompson	Gilesgate Junior Mixed School, Durham
Mr H Turner	Brookhead Junior School, Stockport
Mr G Vaughan-Jones	Ysgol Beca, Clunderwen
Mrs I Welch	Robert Bruce Middle School, Kempston
Mr J Williams	Ysgol y Cymera, Pwllhelli
Mrs M Wiseman	Norton County Primary School, Malton
Mr N Woodhead	Dorridge County Junior School Solihull

Appendix 5

5.1 Membership of the Monitoring Team

The members of the Mathematics Monitoring Team at the NFER responsible for carrying out the mathematics surveys are:

Mr D D Foxman	(Leader)
Mr M J Cresswell	(Deputy leader)
Dr M E Badger	
Mr R M Martini	
Mr P Mitchell	

5.2 APU Steering Group on Mathematics

Mr C H Selby HMI (Chairman – to August 1980) – APU

Mr T A Burdett HMI (Chairman – from August 1980) – APU

Miss J L Atkin HMI	– HM Inspectorate
Dr A W Bell	– The Shell Centre for Mathematical Education, University of Nottingham
Miss M I Boland HMI	– DENI
Mr D D Foxman	– Leader, Mathematics Monitoring Team, National Foundation for Educational Research
Mrs J Holloway	– Fairlight Middle School, Brighton
Mr I R Lloyd	– HM Inspectorate (Wales)
Mr D J Maxwell	– Education Adviser, North Tyneside
Mr G Saltmarsh	– Mathematics Department, Queen Elizabeth's School, Crediton
Mr P J Scott	– Headmaster, City of Leeds School, Leeds
Dr A S Willmott	– National Foundation for Educational Research

5.3 Monitoring Services Unit (NFER)

Mrs B A Bloomfield	(Head of Unit)
Mrs A Baker	
Mrs M Hall	

5.4 Monitoring Group (NFER)

Dr C Burstall	(Chairman)
Mrs B A Bloomfield	
Dr B H Choppin	
Mr D D Foxman	
Dr T Gorman	
Mr A N James	

Mr B Sexton   (Project Statistician)
Dr R Sumner
Dr A S Willmott

5.5 Members of the APU Consultative Committee

Professor J Dancy (Chairman)*   — School of Education, University of Exeter.

Miss J E L Baird   — Joint General Secretary, AMMA
Mr P Boulter   — Director of Education, Cumbria (ACC)
Mr P J Casey   — Deputy Director (Education and Training), CBI
Mr R G Cave   — Senior Education Officer, Cambridgeshire
Mr H Dowson   — Deputy Headmaster, Earl Marshal School,
                                Sheffield (NUT)
Mr P J P Eley   — National Confederation of Parent-Teacher
                                Associations
Professor S J Eggleston   — Department of Education, University of Keele
Mr D Fisher   — County Education Officer, Hertfordshire (ACC)
Mr G S Foster   — Headmaster, The Towers School, Ashford (NUT)
Mr G Hainsworth   — Deputy Education Officer, Manchester (AMA)
Councillor Mrs N Harrison   — London Borough of Haringey (AMA)
  (from July 1980)
Mr K S Hopkins   — Deputy Director of Education, Mid-Glamorgan
                                (WJEC)
Mrs J Hughes   — Director, Macmillan Publishers Ltd
Mr C Humphrey   — Director of Education, Solihull (AMA)
Mr A Jarman   — Education Department, NUT
Dr Kathleen Jones   — Parent and Doctor, Sheffield
Mr T M Jones   — Headmaster, Werneth Junior School, Oldham
  (from June 1980)   (NUT)
Mr J A Lawton   — Chairman, Kent County Council (ACC)
Mr G M Lee   — Doncaster Metropolitan Institute of Higher
  (from September 1980)   Education, (NATFHE)
Mr S Maclure   — Editor, Times Educational Supplement
Mr J W Mansell   — Paddington College (NATFHE)
  (up to September 1980)
Mr J G Owen   — Chief Education Officer, Devon
Mr A M S Poole   — Headmaster, Western School, Mitcham
                                (NAS/UWT)
Dr W Roy   — Headmaster, The Hewett School, Norwich
                                (NUT)
Councillor Mrs A C R Rumbold — Chairman, London Borough of Kingston-upon-
  (up to July 1980)   Thames, Education Committee (AMA)
Professor M D Shipman   — Department of Education, University of
                                Warwick
Mrs A C Shrubsole   — Principal, Homerton College
Mr F A Smithies   — Assistant General Secretary (Education),
                                (NAS/UWT)

* Professor B E Supple was Chairman of the Committee until March 1980

Mr T P Snape   — Headmaster, King Edward VI School, Totnes
                                  (SHA)
Miss R Stephen   — Association of Professional Executive, Clerical
                                  and Computer Staff
Mr D M Wilkinson   — Headmaster, Wolgarston Comprehensive,
                                  Penkridge (NAHT)
Mr D Winters   — Headmaster, Hilton Primary School, Newcastle-
  (up to June 1980)   upon-Tyne (NUT)
Professor J Wrigley   — School of Education, University of Reading
Mr A Yates   — Director, National Foundation for Educational
                                  Research

Appendix 6. Note on the APU

The Assessment of Performance Unit (APU) was set up in 1975 within the Department of Education and Science. It aims to provide information about national levels of performance in a number of curricular areas and across the full ability range.

The terms of reference of the APU are as follows:

> To promote the development of methods of assessing and monitoring the achievement of children at school, and to seek to identify the incidence of under-achievement.

Associated with these terms of reference are the following tasks:

- To identify and appraise existing instruments and methods of assessment which may be relevant for these purposes.

- To sponsor the creation of new instruments and techniques for assessment, having due regard to statistical and sampling methods.

- To promote the conduct of assessment in co-operation with local education authorities and teachers.

- To identify significant differences of achievement related to the circumstances in which children learn, including the incidence of under-achievement, and to make the findings available to those concerned with resource allocation within government departments, local education authorities and schools.

In developing its monitoring programme the APU has been concerned to reflect the breadth of the curriculum in schools and to display the full range of pupil performance. Many school subjects involve mathematical skills and concepts to some degree just as every part of the school curriculum depends upon and makes its own contribution to language development. In the same way scientific development is not solely the product of science teaching, nor does aesthetic awareness grow solely from formal instruction in art, music and drama.

The first APU surveys took place in 1978, in mathematics. English language monitoring began in 1979, and science monitoring in 1980. Monitoring of the first foreign language (French, German and Spanish) will begin in 1983.

Although there is at present no commitment to monitor performance in any other areas, exploratory work is being undertaken to investigate the desirability and feasibility of assessing pupils' performance in the areas of aesthetic, physical and technological development. Some work has also taken place in the field of personal and social development, but it has been decided not to undertake national monitoring in this area.

The assessment procedures in mathematics are developed by the Mathematics Monitoring Team at the National Foundation for Educational Research. Their work is steered by a group consisting of teachers, advisers, teacher trainers, educational researchers and HMI, acting under the overall direction of the Heads of the Unit. The Secretary of State for Education and Science is advised about the work of the Unit as a whole by a Consultative Committee which is broadly representative of local authority and teacher associations, both sides of industry, parents, researchers and the education service generally. Advice about statistical matters and sampling strategy is provided by a Statistics Advisory Group.

The aim of the APU is to produce and make generally available national pictures of pupil performance. The Unit does not produce statements about the performance of individual children, schools or local education authorities. The results of the surveys are published regularly, in the form of reports, by Her Majesty's Stationery Office. This is the third report to be published, and is the second report on the mathematics performance of 11 year olds.

Further information about the work of the APU is available from the Department of Education and Science, Information Division, Room 2/11, Elizabeth House, York Road, London SE1 7PH.

Index

An asterisk against a paragraph reference indicates that a definition or explanation of the term can be found in that paragraph.

(Note: A denotes Appendix)

Printed in England for Her Majesty's Stationery Office by Robendene Ltd., Amersham
Dd 698737 C60 5/81